Face Future

A doctor's collection of stories, biographical glimpses, jokes, poems and practical advice with Christian devotions about health and wellbeing.

BOOK ONE:

Seniors can inspire, apply wisdom and model values

William A. M. Cutting

Onwards and Upwards Publishers
Berkeley House, 11 Nightingale Crescent,
Leatherhead,Surrey, KT24 6PD.
www.onwardsandupwards.org

ISBN: 978-1-907509-97-1

Cartoons: Ann Marsden

Cover design: Leah-Maarit

About the Author

William Cutting was born in South India where his father was a medical missionary and his grandfather had been Principal of a Mission High School in Varanasi (Benares, North India). He trained in medicine at Edinburgh University where he met his wife, Margot, who was also training for medical mission work. They worked in rural India, Andhra Pradesh, for twelve years, developing simple child health services and using nutrition rehabilitation to help mothers feed their malnourished children back to health with local foods.

After six years at the London School of Hygiene and Tropical Medicine and the Tropical Child Health Unit of the Institute of Child Health, Great Ormond Street, he was appointed to the Department of Child Life and Health of the University of Edinburgh with special responsibility for international paediatric trainees. He also acted as consultant with WHO, UNICEF, British Council etc. His research interests were wide. At one time he was responsible for two small international teams. In Bangladesh they studied zinc supplementation and catch-up growth in malnourished children, and in Zaire, HIV infection in children. His work provided him much interesting international experience as well as many contacts and friends.

After retiring in 1998, his wide clinical and pastoral interests turned to the many and varied needs of the elderly. He started to collect material, write for and befriend a circle of older people. The paediatrician metamorphosed into a concerned, amateur geriatrician.

Endorsements

As I'm now approaching the time in my own life when I rather like the idea of being called a 'Senior', this book is not just a delight, but a useful friend to keep to hand. It encourages, entertains, commiserates, understands, accepts, shares, informs and inspires. A great read!

Pam Rhodes
Presenter, BBC Television's SONGS OF PRAISE

Seniors are older people who are rich in years and experiences. ... The encouragement they need now is not the same as when they were young. ... There are many keys to a contented old age, including a sense of purpose, good Christian fellowship, and worship. There is also laughter. Laughter, it is said, strengthens the immune system, boosts energy, diminishes pain and protects from stress.

William Cutting's books for Seniors deliver encouragement and humour, in light, gentle touches. Some are old jokes, but none the worse for that. They can be picked up and put down as the mood dictates, but they will leave readers with a smile and a sense of belonging to a great band of pilgrims who have covered a great distance and are nearly Home.

Louise Morse
Author, Cognitive Behavioural Therapist
Media and Communications Manager for Pilgrim Homes

During these later years of my life I have found many able and intelligent people who have submitted to a very negative attitude to living – a deep, destructive sense of uselessness; an intrusive and corrosive sense of guilt; an overwhelming, crushing self-pity; and often an alarming panic of fear. William's book is an antidote to all of that and so much more – viewing life as a challenge and not a threat; determining to live life to the full and not half-heartedly; realising that life still has a real purpose and relevance bringing richness into the lives of others and fulfilment to our own.

This book is neither pretentious nor patronising but is based on personal experience, accurate observation and downright good humour. Underlying all its encouraging affirmation for those of us of 'riper years' is the conviction that life is a gift from God and so we must start living it in a positive rather than negative way today and not tomorrow.

Rev. Jim Graham
Pastor Emeritus at Gold Hill Baptist Church

Very energising ... a source of inspiration for all generations.

Ann Macfarlane, OBE
Trustee on the Board of the Social Care Institute of Excellence,
Expert by Experience with the Care Quality Commission

Loved the cover and cartoons. ... I was fully absorbed by the stories, and the book pulled me along to discover more. A very useful resource. ... [It's also] the sort of book you [can] dip into [and could be used as a] very good daily devotional book with excellent prayers.

Captain Mike Collyer CA

Voluntary Chaplain to Visitors, Sheffield Cathedral, and
   Facilitator of the Senior's Action Team,
Retired Church Army evangelist and
   trainer in ministry for the elderly

A Biblical perspective on wisdom is that it is a possible, though not an inevitable, outcome of getting older. Church leaders in scripture were called 'elders', as are local leaders in a number of cultures. This is no semantic accident.

William Cutting has written a small series of books, and this first volume is a rich repository of wisdom and some good humour from his life experience. This is a helpful collection and a welcome contribution in a world where eldership (the older generation) can be devalued. It deserves to be widely read.

Lord Bishop of Bristol, Rt Revd Mike Hill

Parliamentary Spokesperson for:
Health, Social Care/Medical Ethics and Criminal Justice

Acknowledgements

Dedication – to my family

To the previous generations who nurtured, encouraged, were great role models, servants of God and of their fellow men and women.

To my wife, Margot, who has supported me so faithfully and brought up our children; to my siblings, Christopher, Janet and Elizabeth ('Butter') who in my own generation have served different communities in exemplary ways.

To our children – Alastair, Catriona, Kenneth and Colin – who continue to encourage and inspire me in their varied and devoted roles, and to our grandchildren who show exciting signs of promise.

Thanks – to a host of inspiring Seniors, all of whom I knew personally...

To devout and spirited Senior people in Edinburgh and Surbiton: George Hossack, Robbie Harkness, Betty Forbes, Archie Dale, Tony Davies, Dick Fincham, Connie Hunt and Lionel Wright.

In India: to Rachel Chacko, P. Zachariah, Mollie Smith, Rajamma David, Purushotham Reddy, G.T. Mark, M. Jayanna Joseph, K.C. Mammen, Ann Bothamley, Lesslie Newbigin and also Father Trevor D'Souza of Mumbai, who gave me a copy of 'The Bible for Seniors' and encouraged me to modify and edit William Barclay's Prayers into the booklet 'Prayers for Seniors'.

To professional medical mentors who were inspirational into their advanced years: John Crofton, Denis Burkitt and David Morley.

Thanks – for contributions

In particular to Ann Marsden, a former colleague in India, who has freely given her time and artistic skill to illustrate and enliven a number of articles.

Also I would like to thank the people who have sent me stories, jokes and poems: Chris Cutting, Andrew Griffiths, Ann Eastburgh, Catriona Allen, Liz Colten, David Bendell, Robert Morley, Norman Allan, Don Harrison, Kier Howard, Robert Schramm and others.

Finally I am very grateful for the guidance and help from Mark and Luke Jeffery, editors at Onwards and Upwards Publishers.

About 'Face the Future'

For many people, old age creeps up on you when you are busy with other things, and very few of us admit to being old. However, "old age is not for wimps"; it brings with it a package of problems that we have to face, live with and adjust to: reduced mobility, failing health, 'forgetfulness', a loss of independence, bereavement and loneliness. But there is much that can be done to *face the future* in a positive manner.

Most Seniors have a heap of things to be thankful for. Many can look back on a wealth of life experiences; many enjoy a degree of security and, by faith in God, can look forward in hope for the big event of old age: death. This is a fact that must not be denied but which, as a Christian, I consider is a new beginning!

The French philosopher, Louis-Vincent Thomas said:

"…only through love, faith and humour can we confront and perhaps transform the terrible realities of old age, decrepitude, and death."[1]

In this series of little books I use this powerful triumvirate of forces to combat what many see as the spectre of old age. Each of these components is important: love, faith and humour. I have woven in many stories and added

---

[1] Louis-Vincent Thomas, quoted by Marie de Hennezel in "The Warmth of the Heart prevents your Body from Rusting", chapter 1 page 13. Published by Rodale, a division of Macmillan, London, 2011.

practical information to help Seniors reduce and deal with some of the physical and social limitations that confront the elderly. Each section is lifted by Ann Marsden's fun pictures, some poems and jokes.

I planned a single volume, but my Editors pointed out that there was too much useful material, that a single volume would be bulky and uncomfortable for the target audience of older people. Smaller volumes would be easier to read and handle. Hence the original book has become a tetralogy.

In **Book One** you can find the inspiration, wisdom and faith of many Seniors who are role models for both the elderly and people of any age.

In **Book Two** you will see something of the vulnerability of Seniors, but also ways in which being grandparents or having a Christian faith can give great fun and fortitude.

Book Three encourages Seniors to face the future by making the most of the health that they have, by keeping moving and by sensible eating and drinking. There are suggestions about making the best use of the health services.

In **Book Four** Seniors can consider practical matters like car driving, dental care, facing dementia and preparing to finish well in this life and move on peacefully and positively. It is by no means a gloomy but a hopeful conclusion.

William A.M. Cutting
MBChB (Edin), FRCPE, FRCPCH

Contents

Terminology

What do others call us?
What should we call ourselves?

Older people are sometimes conscious of their limitations, aches and pains, and then we think of ourselves as 'crocks' or 'crumbles'. At times we feel old-fashioned and we think of ourselves as 'dinosaurs', 'fossils' or 'have-beens'. Though aware of our fragility at times, we are not happy about others referring to us by these names, or even as 'the sunset brigade', as if we are on the way out and sinking fast. These things smack of ageism.

Some names have a hint of the promise or even the power of later years such as 'golden oldies' or 'silver surfers' or 'the great grey vote'. There are also gentler and more neutral titles such as 'the older generation' or 'elders' or 'old folk'. But I have chosen to adopt the single word or name 'Seniors'.

It has limitations, as some have pointed out. You can be senior in years but short in worldly wisdom and vice versa. However, 'Seniors' derives something from the widely used term 'senior citizens', which I do not consider to be demeaning. Rather, I like to think it carries a sense of 'responsible and respected in society'. So in these books you will find the word Seniors used throughout.

Foreword by Fiona Castle

In today's society, youthfulness tends to be admired and old age abhorred. It is true that 'chronological challenge' is real. Many old people fear the disorders and disabilities of body and brain that increase with age.

This is the first of a small series of books, intended as a tonic and antidote for the difficult Senior years. In this book you will find collected; biographical vignettes, moving stories, practical suggestions, jokes, poems, prayers and scriptural devotions. The medical author, from his rich experience of life, has concocted a potent medication of encouragement that will be welcomed by most Seniors. There is a happy mixture of secular and sacred, the factual and the facetious, with stories that are both comic and challenging. It is an amazingly comprehensive collection, which should challenge young, middle-aged and Seniors alike, on a vast range of topics. I would say it is a 'must' for every household!

Fiona Castle OBE
Writer

Introduction

The golden age of senior citizens

The cartoonist Georges Wolinski, in the French weekly, Paris Match, of August 10-16, 2006, has a cartoon strip which is covered by copyright. Fortunately, Ann Marsden, my artistic colleague, has come up with a couple of sketches that effectively capture the scene and theme. Scene: a group of healthy, chatting, laughing senior citizens, happy to be alive, are sharing a snack and a bottle of wine in a bistro.

AEM
after Welmski

At the next table sit a group of young people, shoulders hunched, looking sad and at a loss.

A child standing nearby comments on the scene: "Seventy – that's the age when life begins! They exercise, travel, share memories and joke about their past." He points to the miserable young people. "Look at them. They're worried, grim-faced, unshaven, their shirts hanging out, they don't know how to read, write or express themselves any more. Their girlfriends are goths, tattooed and pierced."

Concluding he says, "You can't imagine how much I'm looking forward to becoming a senior citizen!"

Face the Future

Seniors

can inspire

Face the Future

Seniors in Society

In the arrival hall of the new Terminal 5 at Heathrow airport in London we were waiting for our friend from India. Just in front of us were two young Asian men. One sported a red shirt which declared he was a supporter of Arsenal Football Club. The other was running his finger over the screen of his smartphone but quickly slipped the gadget into his pocket as an elderly Indian couple emerged through the doors. The two young men ran forward eagerly. They both bowed to the ground before the old couple and touched their feet with both hands. It was a moving sign of respect from two modern British men, based on traditional society values.

In our modern Western industrial society which idolises youth, sadly we often see the elderly treated without respect, implying that they only have limited value and may be a burden. In the political arena in Britain the aspiring prime minister, debating with his senior adversary, declared boldly, "You are the past, but I am the future." Not every politician got away with playing the 'age card'. In 1984, the film-star presidential candidate, Ronald Regan, then seventy-three years old, was debating with Walter Mondale, fifty-six. A man in the audience asked Regan if he was up to the stress of the job. With a twinkle in his eye, he replied, "I will not make age an issue of this campaign. I am not going to exploit, for political purposes, my opponent's youth and inexperience."

Older people can and should be characterized in a positive way – as experienced in life, well versed in the ways of the world, and often competent and caring citizens.

The term **ageism**[2] was coined by Dr Robert Butler in 1968. He campaigned for the wellbeing of the elderly and explained that this attitude, ageism, "allows the younger generations to see older people as different from themselves; they subtly cease to identify with their elders as human beings."[3] It stereotypes older people and allows them to be treated in demeaning ways. They have 'had their day', are less capable, less valued and less deserving of treatment or social care. This is a wrong and un-Christian attitude towards the vulnerable which we must check and reject.[4]

In the Bible the elderly are often seen to have a valued place in the scheme of things. In the commandments that God gave, he specifically mentioned that the elderly should be respected. Indeed it is one way of showing respect for God.

> Stand up in the presence of the aged, show respect for the elderly and revere your God. I am the LORD.
>
> *Leviticus 19:32 (NIV)*

---

[2] The term 'ageism' was first published by Dr Robert Butler in 1969 in The Gerontologist, 9, 243-246, under the title 'Age-ism: Another form of bigotry'. He expanded the term over the years and in his most recent and final book, 'The Longevity Prescription: the 8 Proven Keys to a Long, Healthy Life' (The Penguin Group, USA (2010), pp. 73,121) he describes it in this way: "Ageism is the systematic discrimination against people because they are old, or it is the segregation, stereotyping and stigmatizing of people on the basis of age."

[3] The Gerontologist 1969, 9, 243-246

[4] See page 35

In the Psalms, Seniors are very much part of the worshipping community. Above all, God is great, so everyone – all age groups – must praise Him, and this certainly includes the elderly.

> Young men and women, old men and children. Let them praise the name of the LORD, for his name alone is exalted; his splendour is above the earth and the heavens.
>
> *Psalm 148:12-13 (NIV)*

In Psalm 71:18, the writer declares his faith and pleads that when he is old he will have special responsibility to tell the message about God's power to the next generation.

> Even when I am old and grey, do not forsake me, my God, till I declare your power to the next generation, your mighty acts to all who are to come.
>
> *Psalm 71:18 (NIV)*

In the wisdom literature children are advised to listen to the advice of their parents.

> Listen with respect to the father who raised you, and when your mother grows old, don't neglect her.
>
> *Proverbs 23:22 (The Message)*

In fact, the Bible contains many examples of men and women whom God used late in life, often with great effect. The stories of a number of them appear in subsequent chapters.

Prayer

Dear Father God, we thank you that the message of your love is for all, without discrimination.

Dear Father, we thank you that race, colour, gender or age are not important in your eyes. Rather, we are all seen as your children in need of love, care, forgiveness and redemption.

Dear Father, we thank you that your prophets and disciples often remind us that neither appearance nor age are important in your sight, but that you look upon the motives and responses of our hearts. Please purify our motives, and may our hearts respond to your love for us.

Dear Father, we thank you that you are deeply concerned for the vulnerable. Please grant us sympathy for those who are weak and lonely, and give us deeds to demonstrate our concern.

Amen.

Seniors can Inspire Others

It is exciting to see some old folk in their seventies, eighties and beyond still active, alert and brimming with enthusiasm that makes some twenty-year-olds look lethargic. Some Seniors still command companies and lead countries. Others produce new books, plays, paintings or music, and some have won fame in new careers begun only after 'retirement'. Years ago Giuseppe Verdi (1813-1901) wrote 'Falstaff' when over eighty, an opera full of vigour, freshness, emotional intensity and racy humour. Both Palmerston and Gladstone were octogenarian Prime Ministers in Britain, and Benjamin Franklin did some of his best work for his country after he was seventy.

Forget 'Help the Aged'; some of our Seniors in the twenty-first century are far too busy helping others! Queen Elizabeth in her eighties shoulders civic responsibilities that would leave many youngsters exhausted. The octogenarian Pope, Benedict XVI, was knocked to the ground one Christmas Eve but calmly continued the Mass and his full programme without mentioning it. Doris Lessing, a Zimbabwean-British writer, scooped the Nobel Prize for literature at eighty-eight. Both in their eighties, David Attenborough's televised nature programmes are widely acclaimed and Bruce Forsyth introduces 'Strictly Come Dancing' with nifty tap dance. John Stott, a leading Anglican clergyman 'retired' after an influential thirty year ministry at All Souls Church in London, to found the Langham

Partnership International, and ran a worldwide ministry combining evangelism and social action. He still drew large crowds when speaking at the Keswick Convention when eighty-six! A personality giant of our time, Nelson Mandela, took office as the first democratically elected President of South Africa at the age of seventy-six. After retiring from active retirement, he still influenced world affairs!

Sometimes God gives Seniors remarkable responsibilities. He told one couple in the Bible, Abram and Sarai, that they would be the parents of "many nations". They reached old age childless, and when God repeated the promise they laughed because it was so ridiculous. Then God caused them to conceive at a remarkable age and Isaac was born.

> Abram's wife Sarai had not been able to have any children ... Abram was ninety-nine years old when the LORD appeared to him again and said, "I am God All-Powerful. If you obey me and always do right, I will keep my solemn promise to you and give you more descendants than can be counted." Abram bowed with his face to the ground, and God said:
>
> I promise that you will be the father of many nations. That's why I now change your name from Abram to Abraham ... Abraham, your wife's name will now be Sarah instead of Sarai. I will bless her, and you will have a son by her. She will become the mother of nations, and some of her descendants will even be kings.

Abraham bowed with his face to the ground and thought, "I am almost a hundred years old. How can I become a father? And Sarah is ninety. How can she have a child?" So he started laughing.

Genesis 16:1; 17:1-4,15-17 (CEV)

I don't know how they counted years, but God's promise was fulfilled. The wonderful human response was peals of laughter!

Prayer

Dear Lord God, though I lack the gifts of the great and the energy of some, open my eyes and heart to see that you can still use me when I am old.

Help me to help others where I can, and if I lack the strength, give me the words to encourage and the faithfulness to pray.

Amen.

Seniors can Inspire the Young

Robert Butler – the prophet of anti-ageism

In 1927, before he was a year old, Robert Butler's parents split up and he was transferred to the care of his

maternal grandparents on a chicken farm in New Jersey, USA. His grandfather, in his seventies, became his best friend and teacher; but when he was seven, Robert was devastated by his grandfather's sudden death. He then realised that his grandparents were 'old'.

In the Depression, his grandmother lost the farm and they survived on government food subsidies. She found sewing work, and Robert helped by selling papers and mending bicycles. When he was eleven, the cheap hotel in which they were living burnt down with all their possessions. Robert later wrote:

> "What I remember even more than the hardships of those years was my grandmother's triumphant spirit and determination. [She] showed me the strength and endurance of the elderly."

Butler went on to study medicine at Columbia University and then to specialize in psychiatry and researched care of the elderly. He was shocked by the cavalier way his fellow physicians treated elderly patients, and eventually established the Department of Geriatric Medicine at Mount Sinai School of Medicine. Against much scepticism and resistance he persisted until it became mandatory for all medical students to have a one month rotation in geriatrics. He coined the word **ageism** to describe the way that older patients are stereotyped and treated in demeaning and unfair ways. The battle against this discrimination is far from over, and he continued to work at the International Longevity Centre until his death, in July 2010[5], aged eighty-three. Interviewed shortly before he died he declared that fighting for the cause of older people gave his life purpose.

> "[I continue to] put in sixty hours a week and I love every minute of it."

Jesus praised the persistence and endurance of another widow who was the star of one of his stories.

> Then Jesus told his disciples a parable to show them that they should always pray and not give up. He said: "In a certain town there was a judge who neither feared God nor cared what people thought. And there was a widow in that town who kept coming to him with the plea, 'Grant me justice against my adversary.' For some time he refused. But finally he said to himself, 'Even

---

[5] BMJ 2010;341:c4051

though I don't fear God or care what people think, yet because this widow keeps bothering me, I will see that she gets justice, so that she won't eventually come and attack me!'" And the Lord said, "Listen to what the unjust judge says. And will not God bring about justice for his chosen ones, who cry out to him day and night? Will he keep putting them off? I tell you, he will see that they get justice, and quickly. However, when the Son of Man comes, will he find faith on the earth?"

Luke 18:1-8 (NIV)

Note the final challenging personal question that Jesus asks us all.

The heroine and inspiration of Robert Butler's life was his aged grandmother who was a role model of enthusiasm and perseverance. The fruits of her life are still at work through the anti-ageism and positive longevity campaigns pioneered by her grandson.

Prayer

Dear Father God I thank you for the Seniors I have known who have been an inspiration to me. I thank you for the old people I know who are role-models for others. Grant them, O God, the strength and perseverance to continue to inspire others of all ages.

I also pray for the elderly folk I know who are struggling with all sorts of difficulties.

- Bless those who have many aches and pains, arthritis and difficulty in moving.
- Bless those who have illnesses of different sorts and do not get the care they need.
- Bless those who are bereaved and those who feel forgotten, sidelined, isolated and alone.
- Bless those who are afraid of the future, how they will cope or who will look after them.
- Bless those who do not know of your love and the promise that you are waiting to be their friend. Dear Father God, send someone to them with friendship and news of your love in Jesus.

Dear Father, if today I meet any in need, may I be of service in the name of the Lord Jesus.

Amen.

How to Overcome Ageism

Go beyond the stereotypes of ageing that labels people as 'elderly', 'oldies', 'dinosaurs', 'fogeys' or 'fossils'. Even when used in goodhearted fun, such labels do not tell us that though some of these people may have rigid attitudes, diminishing health and capability, many are reliable, creative, great volunteers, caring and fun-loving friends. Most have made great contributions to society. Challenge the myths and language that imply that older adults are less valuable, feel emotional pain less, deserve less care and cost the country more.

Learn more about **ageing** and its difference from **ageism**. Ageing is a natural process which requires understanding, sympathy and support. It should not be the butt of jokes or unkind images. Old people can laugh about their own limitations, but ignorance about the elderly breeds ageism, which stereotypes them, discriminating against them, labelling them a burden on society.

Talk openly about ageism and related issues. Involve Seniors in a range of activities. Don't let ageism and age discrimination remain hidden or an acceptable way to act. Let others see real older people – people who are resourceful, articulate and creative, hard-working, who are valued friends or colleagues. Also include older adults who have some limitations but show that they are not limited in other ways. People who do not fit the stereotype are a powerful way to fight ageism.

Listen to Seniors who have experienced ageism. They can tell how it has affected them. Monitor media and respond to ageist material. Keep a critical eye on the negative ways in which older adults are often portrayed in newspapers, TV programmes, commercials, films and television shows that reach millions of people. Be sensitive about ageism and respond. Write or e-mail the editor, TV sponsors or movie producers.

Speak up about ageism. When someone you know uses ageist language or images, tactfully tell them of the inaccuracy and educate them. When someone disparages a Senior, tells a joke that ridicules them, or makes disrespectful comments about an older person, you can let them know that this is hurtful and that as a Senior you find the comments offensive and harmful.

When a younger person thanks you when you have done or said something useful, he may conclude, "Thanks for that! I'm so glad to see you up and around!" Does he mean, "Good grief, you are ancient, but surprisingly you are still able to be useful."? If you feel justifiably offended by a backhand compliment, a good response to make him think is to say, "Thanks, and I am glad to see you up and around too!" Or, leave the ball in his court by asking, "What did you mean by that?" Then he needs to think about his remark.

Let's watch our own language. Many of us use terms and expressions that may perpetuate ageism. We depersonalize older adults by referring to them as 'the elderly'. In the following sections there are many jokes that involve the way older people react to life and the changes in the world. We know that we look at many things differently and there can be cheeky cross-generation joking without bitterness. Fortunately, many of the older generation make fun of themselves, and as an American journalist once wrote:[6]

> "If you don't learn to laugh at trouble, you won't have anything to laugh at when you're old."

Build bridges between generations. This fights ignorance and strengthens understanding. In many societies the different generations depend on each other, and not simply for child-minding. Youngsters can be the eyes, ears and legs for Seniors, and children learn many informal lessons from elders. The generations realize they are connected to each other throughout the lifespan and affect each other's well-being. This reduces negative attitudes against young and old alike.

Medical models of ageism were once blatant in Britain, signs like:

> "Partnerships available, would suit a young man."

> "Vacancies for new patients in this practice, for those under sixty years of age".

Now the situation is more subtle and complex. Often more young people are accepted for some surgical

---

[6] Edgar Watson Howe 1853-1937

procedures, for example joint replacements, but this can be because some older people also have other diseases which make the procedure a genuine risk.

Encourage political and practical change. Contact your elected representatives. Policies and attitudes that perpetuate ageism can be changed. The political climate is on our side. Pressure on pension funds encourages later retirement, not at some arbitrary 'default' age. Senior employees are often more reliable, friendly and better informed.

Warning, active Seniors!

The Senior residents in an old folks home in Aberdare, Wales, were unhappy about the Department of Transport standard signpost outside their home (two stooped figures with walking stick, see above). They consider that they are very active and created a series of other signs which now warn and welcome visitors who approach their home.

"Will I live to see eighty?"

I recently registered with a new General Practitioner (primary care doctor) who gave me a full physical examination. After the visit and exhaustive lab tests, he said I was doing 'fairly well' for my age. I'd just turned sixty five.

A little concerned about that comment, I couldn't resist asking him, "Do you think I'll live to be eighty?"

He asked, "Do you smoke tobacco, or drink beer, wine or hard liquor?"

"Oh no," I replied, "I'm not doing drugs, either!"

Then he asked, "Do you eat red meat steaks and barbecued ribs?"

I said, "Perhaps once or twice a year. My former doctor said that all red meat is very unhealthy!"

"Do you spend a lot of time in the sun, like playing golf, tennis, boating, sailing, hiking, mountaineering or bicycling?"

"No, I'm not into those things," I explained.

He asked, "Do you gamble, drive fast cars, or have sex frequently?"

"No," I said.

He looked at me and said, "Then, why are you bothered about living long?"

Sadly this General Practitioner has a very limited view of the huge God-given menu of activities and relationships that are open for Seniors to enjoy in life. His patient could still have a full two or three decades of worthwhile, productive and enjoyable life.

This is a sort of ageism joke which all Seniors must overcome with vitality!

More Inspiring Seniors

In the news in 2012

Here are some stories of Seniors whose achievements attracted the attention and admiration of the media in 2012.

The Sony annual Radio Academy Awards are UK's 'Radio Oscars'. In 2012, a couple of ladies from Local Radio Humberside won the Gold for the Best Entertainment Programme, knocking many well-known DJs, comedians and musical duos off their perch. Beryl Renwick, eight-six, and Betty Smith, ninety, have a weekly Saturday evening programme with an audience of twenty thousand. They co-present with BBC's David Reeves, also giving an insight into Humberside's history and Second World War experiences. Their cheerful chat pays little heed to radio convention, and they offer teasing opinions on the contemporary pop they are required to play. ("Madonna has two left legs," Betty recently observed.) The judges praised "a joyous, entertaining double act" who "give a voice to a sector of society unrepresented on radio". Good for them![7]

Oh, and another Sony Gold Award winner was Nicholas Parsons (eighty-eight) for a lifetime in broadcasting, including being host of 'Just a Minute' for over forty-five years.

---

[7] Sony Radio Academy Awards 2012. Best Entertainment Programme: Beryl and Betty – BBC Radio Humberside.

George Beverly Shea, one hundred and two, famous as soloist with Billy Graham's evangelistic team, still alert and sprightly, spent two days sharing his music with prisoners of Louisiana State Jail. Then he travelled to Hollywood to be honoured with a lifetime Grammy Award for his singing career.

Alan Stewart, ninety-seven, from north-east Australia has just completed his forth university degree. With his third degree in law from the University of New England he earned a place in the Guinness Book of Records for the oldest graduate. Now he has another degree in 'clinical science'. He walks daily, meditates and keeps his mind active by playing bridge, and reading medical textbooks and crime novels. (Where does he find time to study?)

Alan says:

"It is never too late to expand your mind, make new friends and challenge yourself to achieve something worthwhile."[8]

Abdul Sattar Edhi, eighty-four, was a refugee from India to Karachi, Pakistan in 1947.[9] Now he is a generous and actively involved philanthropist with many and varied charities. He will accept no funds from Government or religious bodies and would sometimes literally beg on the streets to support his programmes. The Edhi Charitable Foundation now runs the world's largest fleet of over two

---

[8] www.worldrecordacademy.com
[9] His work was briefly described by Hugh Sykes in the BBC's 'From our own correspondent' (2012).

thousand ambulances that virtually replace any national service. It also operates free old people's homes, clinics, orphanages, women's shelters, and rehab centres for drug addicts and those who are mentally ill. Despite his incredible caring networks he is pessimistic. He abhors his country's poverty and corruption which he says "robs the poor of real development". Even at his age he likes nothing better than being a member of an ambulance team responding to an emergency call.

Nicholas Crace, 83, is the oldest living, altruistic kidney donor in the UK. He has given a kidney to an unknown stranger on the NHS waiting list. He said:

> "I knew that seven thousand people were waiting for a kidney, the life of anyone on dialysis is miserable, and one person dies almost every day while waiting for a transplant."

Nicholas, a widower, had fourteen tests over six months before being approved for the operation. He was told that his kidneys functioned as well as someone in their forties.

> "Most of us only need one kidney so it's a sensible thing to do. A living kidney donor makes all the difference to their lives."

Mr Crace, who had been seeking a renewed purpose in life after losing his wife last year, hopes more pensioners will sign up for the donation programme.

> "It's nice at eighty-three to still be of service."

Sometime Seniors have a clearer idea of what is important in life than those who are younger. This was certainly true of Simeon and Anna whose perceptive vision and active devotion is described by Dr Luke and is worth reading again.

> Then when the days stipulated by Moses for purification were complete, they took [Jesus] up to Jerusalem to offer him to God as commanded in God's Law: "Every male who opens the womb shall be a holy offering to God," and also to sacrifice the "pair of doves or two young pigeons" prescribed in God's Law.

> In Jerusalem at the time, there was a man, Simeon by name, a good man, a man who lived in the prayerful expectancy of help for Israel. And the Holy Spirit was on him. The Holy Spirit had shown him that he would see the Messiah of God before he died. Led by the Spirit, he entered the Temple. As the parents of the child Jesus brought him in to carry out the rituals of the Law, Simeon took him into his arms and blessed God:

> God, you can now release your servant; release me in peace as you promised. With my own eyes I've seen your salvation; it's now out in the open for everyone to see: a God-revealing light to the non-Jewish nations, and of glory for your people Israel.

> Jesus' father and mother were speechless with surprise at these words. Simeon went on to bless them, and said to Mary his mother,

This child marks both the failure and the recovery of many in Israel, A figure misunderstood and contradicted – the pain of a sword-thrust through you – but the rejection will force honesty, as God reveals who they really are.

Anna the prophetess was also there, a daughter of Phanuel from the tribe of Asher. She was by now a very old woman. She had been married seven years and a widow for eighty-four. She never left the Temple area, worshiping night and day with her fastings and prayers. At the very time Simeon was praying, she showed up, broke into an anthem of praise to God, and talked about the child to all who were waiting expectantly for the freeing of Jerusalem.

Luke 2:22-38 (The Message)

Prayer

Lord, though I am not as strong or as agile as when I was younger, help me to be sensitive to anyone in distress and quick to respond with friendship and whatever help I can give.

Amen.

Seniors and Friendship in the Digital Age

A teenager sits hunched in front of her computer, eyes glued on the characters below the blue band.

She mutters, "Older people are becoming more and more antisocial." She has pushed her parents into joining Facebook. "Despite all my efforts they only have nineteen friends while I have six hundred and eighty-seven friends. This is living!"

Change scene.

This weekend her mum and dad are out walking and chatting by the river with two other couples, real people! They are spending the day with their real friends while their daughter stares at her virtual friends on Facebook.

"There is nothing on this earth more to be prized than true friendship," wrote the great thirteenth century teacher and theologian Thomas Aquinas. Having friends is truly one of the greatest joys and privileges of life.

In recent months I have had a spate of requests from a range of people asking if I would like to 'be friends'. Some of these are family, some are people I know well, but there are many of whom I know little, friends of children or old work or school acquaintances. Many I have not heard of for years, and others had different interests and attitudes to mine.

Sharing digital information on a website is not friendship. Posting information about yourself on a 'social network' is not friendship; it is writing your diary in public, more like exhibitionism or showing off. You may tell others what you want them to know of your activities, but it says little about character, and character is the most important quality of a good friend. We can only learn about that by sharing something of each other's lives. Friendship is to know and be known as you really are, to build mutual respect, trust and care. It takes time, effort and a willingness to give of yourself. There is a practical limit to how many people you can know and be known by in this personal way.

Take a look at the great examples of quality friendship in the Bible. David and Jonathan (1 Samuel 18:1-4; 23:15-18), Ruth and Naomi (Ruth 1:1-19). The latter friendship crossed cultures and generations. Such true friendships have character quality, personal commitment, emotional intensity, and sacrificial love.

One of the most amazing aspects of the Christian faith is the revelation that friendship is a characteristic of God. It is moving to realise that God desires to be friends with men and women. That was one purpose of his coming to earth in human form, technically called the incarnation. Jesus, the divine Master, said this to his disciples:

> Servants don't know what their master is doing, and so I don't speak to you as my servants. I speak to you as my friends, and I have told you everything that my Father has told me.
>
> *John 15:15 (CEV)*

There is no limit to the number of Facebook friends you can have, but there is a finite limit to the number of real friends you can bond with and enjoy. Most Seniors are thankful for friendships that have lasted a lifetime. They also acknowledge that friendship has to be worked at. It takes time and effort, but it is well worth it.

Prayer

Loving God, thank you for showing your nature and your desire for friendship through the words and the life of Jesus. Please help me accept and experience your friendship.

Loving God, thank you for the gift of friendship with others. Thank you for my friends, both new and old. Especially thank you for friends who have enriched my life by their trust, by their kindness, their affection, their openness, their practical help and their laughter.

Loving God, make me a good friend to others, especially those who have few friends.

Amen.

Senior Wisdom on Friendship

Friends or true friends?

A friend, with a quick click, sent me a musical e-card for my birthday.

A true friend blocked out some time to spend with me on my birthday.

A friend brought a bottle of wine to my party.

A true friend came early to help me cook and stayed late to help me clear up.

A friend, when visiting, acted like a guest.

A true friend felt at home and looked out for ways she could help.

A friend sometimes forgets the names of my children.

A true friend has their numbers on her mobile phone.

A friend invited me in for tea when our house was hit by a power cut.

A true friend gave me a key to her house and said, "Consider it your home till power returns."

A friend sent a 'get well' card when I was at home with pneumonia.

A true friend called in with a cooked meal for the family.

A friend talked to me about my problems.

A true friend seeks every way to help me with my problems.

A friend has never seen me cry.

A true friend sometimes has shoulders wet with my tears.

A friend thinks that the friendship is over when we had an argument.

A true friend knows that disagreements are part of, but not the end of, friendship.

A friend was upset when I called after she had gone to bed.

A true friend asked me why I took so long to call.

A friend expects me to always be there for her.

A true friend expects to always be there for me.

TRAVEL:
The acronym to transport you to real friendship

T is for TRUST

Trust is the glue that holds people together. A relationship will come unstuck without it.

R is for RESPECT

Do not save praise for your friend's funeral tribute. Speak and show your praise and respect now.

A is for AFFECTION

Sometimes affection means love. Sometimes it means a touch. Always it means kindness.

V is for VULNERABILITY

Don't be afraid to let another close. Risk vulnerability, and the relationship will grow.

E is for EMOTIONAL INTIMACY

Learn to be open, to communicate personally and freely. Speak of and show your affection, and a relationship can grow.

L is for LAUGHTER

Enjoy fun and humour together. "Laughter is the shortest distance between two people."

Seniors, Take Time to Talk to Children

A story of friendship across the generations

When I was quite young, my father had one of the first telephones in our neighbourhood. On a polished wooden case, fastened to the wall at the foot of the stairs, hung a shiny receiver. At first I was too little to reach the telephone, but I listened with fascination when my mother talked to it. Then I discovered that inside the wonderful device lived an amazing person. Her name was "Information Please". There was nothing she did not know – anyone's number and the correct time.

My personal experience with the wonderful person in the phone box came one day while my mother was out. I was 'busy' at the tool bench in the basement and hit my finger with a hammer. The pain was terrible, but there was no point in crying because there was no one to give sympathy. I sucked my throbbing finger, saw the telephone, unhooked the receiver and held it to my ear.

"Information, please!" I said into the mouthpiece just above my head.

A small clear voice spoke into my ear. "Information."

"I hurt my finger!" I wailed into the phone; then, with an audience, the tears flowed.

"Isn't your mother at home?" came the question.

"Nobody's home but me," I blubbered.

"Are you bleeding?" the voice asked.

"No," I replied. "I hit my finger with the hammer and it hurts."

"Can you open the icebox?" she asked.

I said I could.

"Then chip off a little bit of ice and hold it to your finger," said the voice.

After that, I called "Information Please" for everything. I asked for help with my Geography, and she told me where Philadelphia was. She helped me with my Maths. "How do I spell 'fix'?" I asked. She told me the best foods for my pet chipmunk.

Then Cheeky, our pet canary, died. I called "Information Please" and told her the sad story. She listened, and tried to sooth my pain, but I was not consoled. I asked her, "Why do birds sing so beautifully and bring joy, only to end up as a heap of feathers?"

She sensed my deep concern, and I never forgot her reply. "Billy, always remember that there are other worlds to sing in."

All this was in a small town in northwest America, but when I was ten years old, we moved east, across the country to Boston. I missed my friend very much. "Information Please" belonged in that old wooden box back home, and I never thought of trying the shiny new phone that sat on the table in the hall. Into my teens, the memories of those childhood conversations never left me. In moments of perplexity or doubt I would recall the serene sense of security

I had had then. How patient, understanding and kind she was to have spent her time on a little boy.

Years later, on my way west to college, I changed planes in Seattle. I had half an hour, and spent fifteen minutes on the phone with my sister, who lived there now. Then, without thinking what I was doing, I dialled my hometown operator and said, "Information, please!"

Miraculously, I heard the small, clear voice I knew so well. I hadn't planned this, but I heard myself saying, "Could you please tell me how to spell 'fix'?"

There was a long pause. Then came the soft spoken answer, "I guess your finger must have healed by now."

I laughed. "So it's really you!" I said. "You have no idea how much you meant to me during that time."

"I wonder," she said, "if you know how much your calls meant to me. I never had any children, and I used to look forward to your calls."

I asked if I could call her again when I came back to visit my sister.

"Please do," she said. "Just ask for Sally."

Six months later I was back in Seattle. I called and a different voice answered, "Information."

I asked for Sally.

"Are you a friend?" she said.

"Yes, a very old friend," I answered.

"I'm sorry to have to tell you," she said, "Sally had been working part-time the last few years because she was sick. She died five weeks ago." Before I could hang up, she added, "Wait a minute! Did you say your name was Billy?"

"Yes!" I answered.

"Well, Sally left a message for you. She wrote it down in case you called. Let me read it to you."

The note said, "Tell him there are other worlds to sing in. He'll know what I mean."

I thanked her – and I knew what Sally meant.

Music in heaven

I saw in heaven another great and marvellous sign: ... They held harps given them by God and sang the song of Moses the servant of God and the song of the Lamb: Great and marvellous are your deeds, Lord God Almighty; just and true are your ways, King of the ages. Who will not fear you, O Lord, and bring glory to your name? For you alone are holy. All nations will come and worship before you, for your righteous acts have been revealed.

Revelation 15:1,3-5 (RSV)

It is good to know there will be music in heaven!

Sources of information change. Encyclopaedias are useful but cumbersome. Google is great – an incredible source of information. Facebook is full of personal news, but it is not like having a real live friend to give you information and advice!

If you have young children in the family, or young friends, spend time in talking to them! It can be a lasting investment and a joy. Never underestimate the positive effect of a few words you may say to a young person.

Listen, my people, to my teaching, and pay attention to what I say. I am going to use wise sayings and explain mysteries from the past, things we have heard and known, things that our ancestors told us. We will not keep them from our children; we will tell the next generation about the Lord's power and his great deeds and the wonderful things he has done.

Psalm 78:1-4 (GNT)

Prayer

Dear Lord, keep our children safe from the dangers of modern technology.

Dear Lord, help us to use modern communication to share happy, helpful and positive messages with the next generation.

Dear Lord, may our young people learn from us of your love and forgiveness.

Amen.

The Girl You Knew at Twenty-Two

The girl you knew at twenty-two
Who heard the vows you made,
Became your wife and shared your life,
May now look slightly frayed.

Others, such fun at twenty-one,
Whom you can still recall,
Find time more kind since in your mind
They have not aged at all.

Think, as you pass the looking glass,
Those laughing girls you knew
Could be the grumpy grandmamas
Who hog your pension queue.

Joe Pamanian

Old Dogs Know Old Tricks

An old German Shepherd dog starts chasing rabbits and squirrels. Before long, he discovers that he cannot catch them as before; also, he's lost. Wandering about, he notices a panther heading in his direction with the intention of having lunch.

The old German Shepherd thinks, "Oh, oh! I'm in deep trouble now!"

Noticing some bones on the ground close by, he immediately settles down to chew on the bones with his back to the approaching cat. Just as the panther is about to leap, the old German Shepherd exclaims loudly, "Boy, that was one delicious panther! I wonder if there are any more around here..."

Hearing this, the young panther halts his attack, a look of terror comes over him and he slinks away into the trees.

"Whew!" says the panther. "That was close! That old German Shepherd nearly had me!"

Meanwhile, a squirrel, who had been watching the whole scene from a nearby tree, figures he can put this knowledge to good use and trade it for some protection from the panther. So, off he goes.

The squirrel soon catches up with the panther and tells him how he was fooled. Then he strikes a deal for himself with the panther.

The young panther is furious at being made a fool of and says, "Here, squirrel, hop on my back and see what's going to happen to that conniving canine!"

Now, the old German Shepherd sees the panther coming with the squirrel on his back and thinks, "What am I going to do now?"

Instead of running, the dog sits down with his back to his attackers, pretending he hasn't seen them yet, and just when they get close enough to hear, the old German Shepherd says loudly, "Where's that squirrel? I sent him off an hour ago to bring me another panther!"

Moral of this story:

Don't mess with the old dogs.
They know when to bluff.
Age and wisdom will overcome youth and treachery.
(But a few old dogs do bluff too much!)

Senior Perks

The life changes that Seniors will notice and may, or may not, enjoy

- In a hostage situation, you are likely to be released early.
- Kidnappers are not very interested in you (unless you are a multimillionaire).
- People call at 9 p.m. (or 9 a.m.) and ask, "Did I wake you?"
- People no longer view you as a hypochondriac.
- There is nothing left to learn the hard way (except new electronic gadgets).
- Things you buy now won't wear out.
- You can eat supper at 4 p.m.
- You no longer think of speed limits as a challenge.
- You sing along with music in lifts (if the songs are old enough).
- Your joints are more accurate meteorologists than the national weather forecasting service.
- Your secrets are safe with your friends because they can't remember them.
- Your quantity of brain cells is finally down to a manageable number.
- You can live without sex but not your glasses.
- Your eyes cannot get much worse (you hope).

Senior Hands Tell a Life Story

Michelle enjoyed art but had a passion for photography. When she left school she was delighted she had earned a place in the photography course of the local Art College. It was a happy marriage of her favourite subjects with exciting scope for her lively imagination!

She was a little disappointed when her first homework assignment was to "take a picture that tells the story of the older generation". She felt at a loss; she was a modern young person, living in the present and looking at the future, and did not like the idea of looking backward at a 'has been' generation.

Her mum said, "Why don't you visit your great grandma in the Old Folks Home. She has seen a lot of life and can still talk about bygone time. She could come up with some ideas." Reluctantly, she took the bus to the edge of town, located the home and this aged relative. Despite her wrinkled face, she had shining eyes and a ready smile in exchange for the bunch of carnations that Michelle handed her.

After a few minutes' chat the old lady reached out and held Michelle's hand. She was shocked because it was bony and deformed, but the grip was firm and the wrinkled skin was soft and warm. The hand was misshaped by arthritis, had dark patches and wrinkles on the back, and an obvious scar on one forefinger.

The old lady saw Michelle staring at her hands and said, "These old hands don't look good now, but they have served me well for ninety years and they have a story to tell! These hands held a slate at school when I learnt to read and write – long, long before ballpoint pens had been invented."

She touched the gold ring on her fourth finger. No way could it get off over her swollen knuckle. "Your great granddad worked overtime in his factory for three months to earn the money for this, and then slipped it proudly onto the finger of his beautiful, blushing bride on her wedding day. When your grandma was born, these hands gently held that tiny baby. When that baby grew up these hands were still lively and knitted the shawl which wrapped her baby – and that baby was your Mum! These hands have wiped away the tears of my children, they have been clenched in righteous anger, and they trembled with anxiety when my son went off to war. These hands have worked in the kitchen garden and prepared thousands of meals for three generations of family. In my haste one day, chopping vegetables, I cut this finger deeply," and she pointed to the scar. "When your great granddad died these hands closed his eyelids and laid him out before he was buried. Yes, they are now deformed, but they are well worn!"

The old lady paused as she felt Michelle grip her hand more tightly, and when she looked up she saw tears run down the young girl's face.

The next week Michelle assembled her gran, her mum, her sister Tracey and her sister's baby Tina and took them all to the Old Folks Home to see Great Grandma. There she took the photograph of five generations of hands that won her the class photography prize.

Photograph source:
The UN Women's Report Program and Network

The Hands of Jesus

Lord Jesus, I thank you for your hands and the way that you used them.

Lord, I think of your well-worn, calloused, working hands. Hands that had held the tools of your trade: hammer, chisel and saw. Hands that had made quality furniture for people and comfortable yokes for oxen.

Lord, I think of your gentle hands that had picked up babies, hands that rested in blessing on the heads of children.

Lord, I think of your loving hands that touched the eyelids of the blind and held the deformed limbs of those with leprosy. Hands that brought healing.

Lord, I think of your open and generous hands that accepted the lunch of a young lad and multiplied it for a multitude of hungry folk.

Lord, I think of your merciful hands that wrote in the sand – while the accusers of the adulterous woman slunk off in shame at your challenge.

Lord, I think of your strong hands that threw out selfish men, merchants who made the Temple for worship into a money market.

Lord, I think of your thankful hands that held up and broke the loaf and poured the wine, and changed for ever these foods into symbols of your love.

Lord, I think of your wounded hands, damaged by heavy nails roughly hammered through sensitive tissues at your crucifixion.

Lord, I think of your scarred hands, shown as evidence of your reality and love to a doubting disciple.

And now Lord, in this busy and often hard world, you have to use my hands, our hands, to do your work. What a privilege and responsibility that is!

So please grant us your help, that our hands may be...

- **skilful** but **well worn** in the service of others;
- **sensitive** to feel the sweat of fear or the feeble pulse, **gentle** when we have to handle delicate issues or sore situations;
- **loving** when we touch those in pain, fear or distress, **merciful** when they have to be used to restrain or punish;
- **open** to receive the gifts from you and from others, but open and **generous** to share with others what we have been given;
- **thankful** as we put our hands together in prayer;
- even **wounded** if we can share in our lives something of your loving sacrifice.

Through your Spirit, Lord Jesus –

may we feel your hand resting on our lives today;

may we feel your touch in any sore or difficult issue today;

may we put our small hands into your loving and powerful hands today.

Amen.

Face the Future

Seniors

can apply wisdom

Face the Future

"Live With Love, and Fear Nothing"

Harry Secombe

"If you have lived your life with love, you will have nothing to fear."

These are the words from the last line of the poem 'On Growing Old', written by Harry Secombe, one of the best loved British comedians of the 20th century.

SIR HARRY SECOMBE, 1921-2001

He was a "comic genius" and "an inspired Goon who made millions laugh", declared his obituaries. He had the voice of a Welsh opera star and a wicked wit.

He first sang in the choir of St. Stephen's Church in Swansea, Wales, which he attended with all of his family. His first comic performances were with his sister Carol in church socials. In 1938 he joined the Army, the Royal Artillery, and served in North Africa and Sicily, and by the time they reached Italy his services were more valued as a member of an entertainment group. After demobilisation he teamed up with Spike Milligan and Peter Sellers, in a series that became

69

'The Goon Show', in which Secombe, playing Neddie Seagoon, was the focus of a range of absurd and unlikely plots. This ran for nearly ten years, and both Milligan and Sellers credited him and his ability to break into song when the act faltered, keeping it on the bill when producers wanted to cut them.

The programme had cult status, and Prince Charles was one of many long term admirers. Countless shows, musicals and films followed. One memorable part was as Mr Pickwick based on Dickens' 'The Pickwick Papers', which gave him a hit single with the song 'If I Ruled the World'. He loved the opera, and could have starred, but friends said that he always feared that he might break into giggles in a serious aria.

In 1948 he had married Myra, a girl from Swansea, and they were married for more than fifty years. He always credited Myra with keeping his feet on the ground. They had four children. Harry came bouncing in and announced that he had just signed a contract with the London Palladium at £1000 a week. "That's nice," said Myra. "Now upstairs you go and spend some time with young Andrew; he's got the measles."

In later life he extended his audience, singing hymns and presenting religious programmes like BBC's 'Songs of Praise'. He had a series of serious illnesses: diabetes, peritonitis, a heart attack, two strokes and cancer of the prostate. It was typical of him that after his first stroke, in his desire to help others with the condition, he agreed to the filming of a BBC documentary, 'The trouble with Harry', which charted his progress for eight months after his stroke. This inspirational programme saw him bravely struggling to overcome the paralysing effect of the stroke through intensive physio-therapy, lots of determination, and the help of his strong religious convictions. After his first stroke he wrote the poem shown below.

On Growing Old

I want the mornings to last longer and the twilight to linger; I want to clutch the present to my bosom and not let it go;

I resent the tyranny of the clock in the hall nagging me to get on with the day;

I am a time traveller but a traveller who would rather walk than fly;

AND YET:

There is a lot to be said for getting old;

The major battles in life are over, but minor skirmishes may still occur;

There is an armistice of the heart, a truce with passion;

Compromise becomes preferable to conflict and old animosities blur with time;

There is still one last hurdle to cross

and the joy of your life measures your reluctance to approach it;

But if you have lived your life with love there will be nothing to fear

for a warm welcome will await you on the other side.

"...if you have lived your life with love..." The love that Harry writes about, the love that he had grown up with, was the love described by Jesus in his stories and his teaching.

It was the unconditional love of a father for his prodigal son, the parable of God's love.

The parable of the Father's love

Jesus continued: "There was a man who had two sons. The younger one said to his father, 'Father, give me my share of the estate.' So he divided his property between them.

"Not long after that, the younger son got together all he had, set off for a distant country and there squandered his wealth in wild living. After he had spent everything, there was a severe famine in that whole country, and he began to be in need. So he went and hired himself out to a citizen of that country, who sent him to his fields to feed pigs. He longed to fill his stomach with the pods that the pigs were eating, but no one gave him anything.

"When he came to his senses, he said, 'How many of my father's hired servants have food to spare, and here I am starving to death! I will set out and go back to my father and say to him: Father, I have sinned against heaven and against you. I am no longer worthy to be called your son; make me like one of your hired servants.' So he got up and went to his father.

"But while he was still a long way off, his father saw him and was filled with compassion for him; he ran to his son, threw his arms around him and kissed him.

"The son said to him, 'Father, I have sinned against heaven and against you. I am no longer worthy to be called your son.'

"But the father said to his servants, 'Quick! Bring the best robe and put it on him. Put a ring on his finger and sandals on his feet. Bring the fattened calf and kill it. Let's have a feast and celebrate. For this son of mine was dead and is alive again; he was lost and is found.' So they began to celebrate."

Luke 15:11-24 (NIV)

We may not have wandered off as far as the prodigal, but we all need to remember and consider our need for God's forgiveness. We need to repent and accept his unconditional love afresh.

The Clown's Prayer[10]

The clown's prayer was read at Harry Secombe's funeral by his grandson Sam.

As I stumble through this life,
help me to create more laughter than tears,
dispense more cheer than gloom,
spread more cheer than despair.

Never let me become so indifferent,
that I will fail to see the wonders in the eyes of a
	child,
or the twinkle in the eyes of the aged.

Never let me forget that my total effort is to cheer
	people,
make them happy, and forget momentarily,
all the unpleasantness in their lives.

And in my final moment,
May I hear You whisper:
"When you made My people smile, you made Me
	smile."

---

[10] Author unknown.

Senior Wisdom Gleaned from the Journey of Life

"I started out in life with nothing, and I still have most of it."

"Maybe it's true that life begins at fifty. But after that everything else starts to wear out, fall out, or spread out."

"Wisdom sometimes comes with old age, but sometimes old age comes alone."

"It was a whole lot easier to get older than to get wiser."

"I finally got my head together, and now my body is falling apart."

"Time may be a great healer but it's a lousy beautician."

"Wrinkles don't hurt, thank goodness!"

"If God wanted me to touch my toes, he'd have put them on my knees."

"Now my wild oats are mostly enjoyed with prunes and oat bran."

"The only difference between a rut and a grave is the depth."

"There are three signs of old age. The first is your loss of memory. I forget the other two."

"Funny, I don't remember being absent-minded."

"If 'all is not lost', then where on earth is it?"

"Some days, you're the top dog; some days you're the lamppost."

"The world only beats a path to your door when you're in the bathroom."

"When I'm finally holding all the right cards, everyone wants to play chess."

"It's frustrating that now when you know all the answers, nobody bothers to ask you the questions."

"Statistics show that at the age of eighty there are five women to every man. Isn't that a bad time for a guy to get those odds?"

"It's hard to make a comeback when you haven't been anywhere."

"It's hard to be nostalgic when you can't remember anything."

"Inside every older person is a younger person wondering what happened, and trying to get out."

"Laughing is good exercise. It's like jogging on the inside."

Teach us to number our days, that we may gain a heart of wisdom.

Psalm 90:12

Cheerful Thoughts for Seniors

"I'm not young enough to know everything."

J.M. Barrie

"When I grow up, I want to be a little boy."

Joseph Heller

"No wise man ever wished to be younger."

Jonathan Swift

"I look forward to being older; then what you look like becomes less of an issue – and what you are is the point."

Susan Sarandon

"When it comes to staying young, a mindlift beats a facelift any day."

Marty Bucella

"Wrinkles should merely indicate where smiles have been."

Mark Twain

"If wrinkles must be written on our faces, let them not be written upon the hearts. The spirit should never grow old."

James A. Garfield

"When grace is joined with wrinkles, it is adorable. There is an unspeakable dawn in happy old age."

Victor Hugo

"Some people, no matter how old they get, never lose their beauty – they merely move it from their faces into their hearts."

Martin Buxbaum

"You're ageing when your actions creak louder than your words."

Milton Berle

"To be eighty years young is sometimes more cheerful and more hopeful, than to be forty years old."

Oliver Wendell Homes

"If I'd known I was gonna live this long, I'd have taken better care of myself."

Eubie Blake
On reaching 100

"Growing old is no more than a bad habit which a busy man has no time to form."

Andre Maurois

"Even when you are old I will be the same. And even when your hair turns white, I will help you. I will take care of what I have made. I will carry you, and will save you."

The prophet Isaiah
Speaking the words of God
Isaiah 46:4 (NLV)

"You don't stop laughing because you grow old, you grow old because you stopped laughing."

Michael Moncur

"Age is not important unless you're a cheese"

Helen Hayes

"The fountain of youth is dull as paint,
Methuselah is my own patron saint.
I've never been so comfortable before."
Oh, I'm so glad I'm not young anymore."

Alan Jay Lerner
from 'Gigi', 1958

Seniors can be Great Students

The story of Rose

The first day of college, our professor introduced himself and challenged us to take a few minutes to get to know someone new. I stood up to look around, when a gentle hand touched my shoulder. I turned around to find a wrinkled little old lady beaming up at me with a smile that lit up her entire being.

She said, "Hi, handsome! My name is Rose. I'm eighty-seven years old. May I give you a hug?"

I laughed and enthusiastically responded, "Of course you may!" and she gave me a squeeze that took my breath away.

"Why are you in college at such a young, innocent age?" I asked.

She jokingly replied, "I'm here to meet a rich husband, get married, and have a couple of kids."

"No, seriously," I asked. I was curious about what motivated her to take on this challenge at her age.

"The first time I went to College I *did* find and marry the rich husband, and had a couple of kids – but I never completed my education. Now my husband is dead I have the opportunity to complete what I started!"

After class we walked to the student union and shared a chocolate milkshake. We became instant friends. Every day for the next three months we would leave class together and talk non-stop. I was always mesmerized listening to this 'time machine' as she shared her wisdom and experience.

Over the year, Rose became a college campus icon and easily made friends wherever she went. She involved herself in everything. She also loved to dress up, and she revelled in the attention bestowed upon her by the other students. She was living it up.

At the end of the year we invited Rose to speak at the graduation dinner. I'll never forget what she taught us. She was introduced and stepped up to the microphone. As she began to deliver her prepared speech, she dropped her cue cards on the floor. Frustrated and a little embarrassed she leaned forward and simply said, "I'm sorry I'm so jittery. Forget the speech! I'll share a few thoughts...

- "You've got to have a dream. Even when you are old in years you should have a dream. When you lose your dreams, you die. We have so many people walking around, even young ones, who are dead and don't even know it!
- "You do not stop doing things because you are old. You will feel old if you stop doing things! You do not stop playing because you are old; you grow old because you stop playing. (Yes, but arthritis is a bit limiting!)
- "The elderly usually don't have regrets for what they did, but rather for things they did not do. The saddest old folk are those with regrets, regrets about what they didn't attempt to do.

- "Growing older just happens. It is mandatory. It doesn't take any talent or initiative. The challenge is to grow wiser, to mature by always finding opportunity in any change which overtakes your life.
- "Humour is a longevity elixir. Every day keep eyes wide open to find something funny. You must have a good laugh every day."

Rose concluded her speech by courageously singing a song about 'The Rose'.

At the year's end, Rose finished the college degree she had begun all those years ago.

One week after graduation, Rose died peacefully in her sleep. Amazingly, over a thousand college students attended her funeral in tribute to the wonderful woman who taught by example that it's never too late to be all you can possibly be.

The Rose

Some say love, it is a hunger,
An endless aching need.
I say love, it is a flower,
And you its only seed.

When the night has been too lonely
And the road has been too long,
And you think that love is only
For the lucky and the strong,
Just remember in the winter
Far beneath the frozen snows
Lies the seed that with the sun's love
In the spring becomes the rose.

Amanda McBroom

Light Years

I met a man from Hindustan
Who wore his years so lightly.
He seemed no more than half his score.
"How come?" I begged, politely.

"The trick with age", replied the sage,
"Is 'Have no business with it.
Try not to ask how long life lasts
 But just enjoy and live it.'"

Based on a poem by Jean Hayes

Pertinent proverbs

"As long as you are learning, you are not old."

"One thing I have learnt is that I still have much to learn."

"You are never too old to set another goal or dream another dream."

C.S. Lewis.

"The happiest of people don't necessarily have the best of everything; they just make the most of everything they have."

Prayer

Thank you, Lord God, for inspirational old people whom I have met and known. (Take a moment to remember them, how they made a difference to you and others.)

Thank you, Lord, for their vision, for their enthusiasm to keep learning and that they could still enjoy life.

Thank you, Lord, for their inspirational wisdom and their drive to keep going through difficulties.

Thank you, Lord, that many were always alert for opportunities to help others and also to see and share the fun in life.

Lord, please grant me a measure, in my own life, of these virtues of saintly Seniors.

Amen.

"Senior Special Breakfast – £2.99"

We went to breakfast at a restaurant where the 'Senior Special' was coffee, two eggs, bacon, hash browns (potato rissoles with onion) and toast for £2.99.

The waitress sized us up. "Would you like the 'Senior Special'?"

"Sounds good," my wife said, "but I don't want the eggs."

"Then, I'll have to charge you three pounds and fifty pence because you're ordering à la carte," the waitress warned her.

"You mean I'd have to pay for not taking the eggs?" my wife asked incredulously.

"YES!" stated the waitress.

"I'll take the special then," my wife said.

"How do you want your eggs?" the waitress asked.

"Raw and in the shell," my wife replied. She took the two eggs home and baked a cake.

Don't mess with Senior ladies! They've been around the block more than once!

Seniors should "Speak the Truth in Love"

In the courtroom of a small town, the Advocate (Attorney) for the Prosecution called his first witness to the stand in a trial. She was a Senior, a grandmotherly, elderly woman. She very solemnly took the oath to tell the truth, the whole truth and nothing but the truth. Then the Avocate asked her, "Mrs. Jones, do you know me?"

She responded, "Why, yes, I do know you, Mr. Williams. I've known you since you were a young boy. And frankly, you've been a big disappointment to me. You lie, you cheat on your wife, you manipulate people and talk about them behind their backs. You think you're a rising legal star when you haven't the brains to realize you never will amount to anything more than a second rate paper pusher. Yes, I know you all right."

The lawyer was stunned. Struggling to find a response, he pointed across the room and asked, "Mrs. Jones, do you know the Advocate for the Defence?"

She again replied, "Why, yes I do. I've known Mr. Bradley since he was a youngster, too. Indeed I used to babysit him for his parents. And he, too, has been a real disappointment to me. He's lazy, bigoted, and he has a drink problem. The man can't build a normal relationship with anyone, and his legal practice is one of the worst in the country. Yes, I know him."

At this point, the Judge, with some difficulty, rapped the courtroom to silence and called both lawyers to the bench.

In a very quiet voice, he said with menace, "If either of you asks her if she knows me, you'll be jailed for contempt of court!"

> "I love you, and because I love you, I would sooner have you hate me for telling you the truth, than adore me for telling you lies."
>
> *Pietro Aretino*

Before speaking, ask yourself, is what I am going to say (a) true? (b) helpful? (c) kind? After three yeses, you may speak out!

> ...we will speak the truth in love, growing in every way more and more like Christ, who is the head of his body, the church.
>
> *Ephesians 4:15 (NLT)*

87

Seniors should Model Truth-Telling

We were dressed and ready to go out for the New Year Party. We turned on a nightlight and the telephone answering machine. Next we covered our pet parakeet and put the cat in the backyard. Finally we phoned the local cab company and requested a taxi cab.

The taxi arrived and we opened the front door to leave the house. The cat we had put out in the yard scooted back into the house. We didn't want the cat shut in the house because she always tries to eat the bird.

I went out to the taxi, while my elderly husband went inside to get the cat. The cat ran upstairs, with my husband in hot pursuit. Waiting in the cab, I didn't want the driver to know that the house would be empty for the night. So I explained to the cab driver that my husband would be out soon. "He's just going upstairs to say goodbye to Grandma."

A few minutes later, he returned, dusted himself down and got into the cab. "Sorry I took so long," he said, as we drove away. "The stupid bitch was hiding under the bed. I had to poke her with a walking stick to get her to come out! Then she tried to escape so I grabbed her by the neck. She was scratching so I had to wrap her in a blanket. But it worked! I hauled her fat ass downstairs and threw her out into the backyard!"

The cab driver hit a parked car!

This is allegedly a true story from a friend who was at school with me in India.

Beware of lies; even the little ones can cause damage. How much did it cost to repair the taxi cab and the other vehicle? Damage to human hearts is even more costly.

In the short list of seven things that God hates and detests, according to the book of Proverbs (6:16-19), two involve lying: "a lying tongue" and "a false witness who tells lies".

Question: What is a lie?

Answer: Any false statement made with deliberate intent to deceive.

Read the sorry story of Ananias and Sapphira in Acts 5:1-9. In that situation it was a fatal error!

Not every falsehood is a lie! Often a simple Senior can err. If someone asks me the ages of my grandchildren, I tell what I believe is the truth. Quite often I make a mistake; years pass so quickly. Have I lied?

If I know the truth and knowingly tell what is untrue, I have lied.

"Honesty is telling the truth to other people. Integrity is telling the truth to myself."

Spencer Johnson

"Always tell the truth. That way you don't have to remember what you said."

"When in doubt, tell the truth."

Mark Twain

Prayer

Dear Lord, I truly value integrity, but I find it easy, just ever so little, to bend the truth when it suits me.

Lord, teach me that every dishonesty is a betrayal of myself, of others and of You.

Lord, forgive me when I am less than completely honest, and guide me in the straight way.

Amen.

Seniors Know About Planting Seeds, and Reaping.

In the store of life

A man was browsing in a big old-fashioned store, a shop full of treasures and surprises. Then he made a shocking discovery: it was God who was behind the sales counter.

The man walked over and asked, "What are You selling?"

God replied, "What does your heart desire?"

The man said, "I want happiness, peace of mind, and freedom from fear – for me and the whole world."

God smiled and said, "I don't sell fruit here. Only seeds."

Paul, writing to his friends in the new Christian churches, was clear about this relationship – the importance of planting good seed if you want a good harvest. God gives some great seeds, but we have to make sure that they are planted well and nurtured properly (see Luke 8).

To one group of Christians he wrote:

Finally, brothers and sisters, whatever is true, whatever is noble, whatever is right, whatever is pure, whatever is lovely, whatever is admirable – if anything is excellent or praiseworthy – think about such things. Whatever you have learned or received or heard from me, or seen in me – put it into practice. And the God of peace will be with you.

Philippians 4:8-9 (NIV)

To another church Paul wrote about this principle. Having planted the good seeds by thinking good thoughts and nurturing them with good actions, putting them into practice, you will eventually produce a good harvest; indeed, they have been called the fruit of God's Holy Spirit.

But the fruit of the Spirit is love, joy, peace, patience, kindness, goodness, faithfulness, gentleness and self-control. Against such things there is no law.

Galatians 5:22-23 (NIV)

A man reaps what he sows.

Galatians 6:7b (NIV)

Seniors can sow seeds, even though they may not always live long enough to see the fruit. Sowing good seed correctly and nurturing young plants well is so important.

Unfortunately, often the opposite is also true; if you sow bad seed, the fruit will be disappointment, distress and bitterness.

Enjoy the freedom to think, speak and behave... badly. Then see where it gets you!

Prayer

Lord God, even as a Senior I sow seeds into the hearts and
minds of others.
May my words and deeds be seeds of love, joy, peace,
patience, kindness, goodness, faithfulness, gentleness
and self-control.
Amen.

You reap what you sow – and how attitudes changed in America

After the suicide attacks on September 11th and the
school massacres in the USA and Canada, someone asked,
"How could God let this happen?"

A Christian leader in the USA pondered and replied, "I
believe God is deeply saddened by these events, just as we
are, but for years we've been telling God to get out of our
schools, to get out of our government and to get out of our
lives. And being the gentle, considerate person He is, I
believe He has calmly backed out. How can we expect God
to give us His blessing and His protection if we demand He
leave us alone?"

In light of recent events, terrorist attacks, school
shootings, the growth of violence in every part of life, even in
the home, where does this behaviour come from? Perhaps it
started when Madeleine Murray O'Hair, a prominent
personality, complained she didn't want prayer in our
schools, and we said, "Okay."

Then someone said, "You'd better not read the Bible in school; that's indoctrination. The Bible says you must not kill, you must not steal, but love your neighbour as yourself." And we said, "Okay."

Then a prominent paediatrician said we shouldn't spank our children when they misbehave because their little personalities would be warped and we might damage their self-esteem. We said an expert should know what he's talking about. And we said, "Okay."

Then someone said that teachers and principals should not discipline our children when they misbehave. The school administrators said, "No faculty member in this school may touch a student when they misbehave because we don't want any bad publicity, and we surely don't want to be sued." (There's a big difference between disciplining, touching, smacking, beating, humiliating, kicking, etc.) And we said, "Okay."

Then some wise school board member said, "Since boys will be boys and they're going to do it anyway, let's give our sons all the condoms they want so they can have all the fun they desire, and we won't have to tell their parents they got them at school." And we said, "Okay." Then someone said, "And let's permit our daughters to have abortions if they want, and they won't even have to tell their parents." And we said, "Okay."

Then some of our top elected officials said, "It doesn't matter what we do in private as long as we do our jobs." Agreeing with them, we said, "It doesn't matter to me what anyone, including the President, does in private as long as I have a job and the economy is good."

Then someone said, "Let's print magazines with pictures of nude women and call it wholesome, down-to-earth appreciation for the beauty of the female body." And we said, "Okay." And then someone else took that appreciation a step further and published pictures of nude children, and then further again by making them available on the Internet. And we said, "Okay. They're entitled to free speech." Then the industry said, let's make TV shows and movies that promote profanity, violence, and illicit sex. Let's record music that encourages rape, drugs, murder, suicide, and satanic themes. And we said, "It's just entertainment. It has no adverse effect. Nobody takes it seriously anyway, so go right ahead."

Now we're asking ourselves why our children have no conscience, why they don't know right from wrong, and why it doesn't bother them to kill strangers, their classmates, and themselves. Probably, if we think about it long and hard enough, we can figure it out. I think it has a great deal to do with "we reap what we sow".

Paul wrote to the Christians in Galatia the following warning:

> Don't be misled: No one makes a fool of God. What a person plants, he will harvest. The person who plants selfishness, ignoring the needs of others – ignoring God – harvests a crop of weeds. All he'll have to show for his life is weeds! But the one who plants in response to God, letting God's Spirit do the growth work in him, harvests a crop of real life, eternal life. So let's not allow ourselves to get fatigued doing good. At the right time we will harvest a good crop if we don't give up, or quit. Right now, therefore, every time we get the chance, let us work for the benefit of all, starting with the people closest to us in the community of faith.
>
> *Galatians 6:7-10 (The Message)*

Eliphaz, speaking in the wisdom book of Job, said:

> In my experience, only those who plant seeds of evil harvest trouble...
>
> *Job 4:8 (CEV)*

What My Mother Taught Me

Seniors, do you remember what you learnt from your mother? Add lessons to the list below, and share these things with the next two generations!

My mother taught me to **appreciate cleanliness** and **a job well done.**

"If you're going to kill each other, do it outside. I just finished cleaning in here."

My mother taught me about **time travel.**

"If you don't tidy your things up, I'm going to knock you into the middle of next week!"

My mother taught me the need for **religion.**

"You'd better pray that stain will come out of the carpet."

My mother taught me **logic.**

"Because I said so, that's why."

My mother taught me **more logic.**

"If you fall out of that swing and break your neck, you're not going out shopping with me."

My mother taught me **foresight**.

"Make sure you wear clean underwear, in case you're in an accident."

My mother taught me **irony**.

"Keep bawling like that, and I'll give you something to cry about."

My mother taught me about **contortionism**.

"Will you just take a look at that dirt on the back of your neck!"

My mother taught me about the science of **transdermal absorption** (through the skin).

"Shut your mouth and eat your supper."

My mother taught me about **endurance**.

"You'll sit there until all that spinach is gone."

My mother taught me about **weather** reporting.

"This room of yours looks as if a tornado went through it."

My mother taught me about **fashion**.

"Put on your tie and your raincoat. It's cold and wet out there. Forget fashion."

My mother taught me **extra sensory perception**.

"Put your sweater on; don't you think I know when you are cold?"

My mother taught me about **honest talking**.

"If I told you once, I've told you a million times. Don't exaggerate!"

My mother taught me **genetics**.

"My giddy goat, you're just like your father."

My mother told me about **behaviour therapy**.

"Stop acting like your father!"

My mother taught me the **circle of life**.

"I brought you into this world. Behave like that and I can take you out of it."

My mother taught me about **envy**.

"There are millions of less fortunate children in this world who don't have wonderful parents like you do."

My mother taught me about **anticipation**.

"Just wait until we get home."

My mother taught me about **receiving**.

"You are going to get it when you get home!"

My mother taught me about the **aetiology of disease**.

"If you don't stop crossing your eyes, they'll get stuck that way."

My mother taught me **humour**.

"When that lawn mower cuts off your toes, don't come running to me."

My mother taught me **how to become an adult**.

"If you don't eat your vegetables, you'll never grow up."

My mother taught me about **my roots**.

"Shut that door behind you. Do you think you were born in a barn?"

My mother taught me about **justice**.

"One day you'll have kids, and I hope they turn out just like you."

My mother taught me **compassion** and **courage**.

"If Tiny Tim is being bullied in the playground, you be his best friend."

My mother taught me **wisdom**.

"When you get to be my age, you'll understand these things."

My son, keep your father's command and do not forsake your mother's teaching. Bind them always on your heart; fasten them round your neck. When you walk, they will guide you; when you sleep, they will watch over you; when you awake, they will speak to you.

Proverbs 6:20-21 (NIV)

NOTE

Some of these valuable lessons have been pushed off the Family Curriculum. One daughter rang Childline and threatened to take her mother to court for "verbal abuse"!

What Mothers Said to Famous Seniors

The mother of **Goldilocks**

"I've got a bill here for a broken chair from the Bear family. Goldie, do you know anything about this?"

The mother of **Mary**

"Look, Mary, how is it that you come home with your clothes filthy and your pet lamb comes home so clean? You'll do your own washing in future."

The mother of **Little Miss Muffet**

"Well, all I've got to say is, if you don't get off your tuffet and start cleaning your room, there'll be a lot more spiders around!"

The mother of **Jonah**

"That's a nice story, but now tell me where you've really been for the last three days."

The mother of **Mona Lisa**

"Wipe that stupid smile off your face, Mona, and admit you ate the last chocolate!"

The mother of **Michelangelo**

"Mike, can't you paint on walls like other children? Do you have any idea how hard it is to get that stuff off the ceiling?"

The mother of **Christopher Columbus**

"I don't care what you've discovered, Christopher. You still could have written!"

The mother of **Napoleon**

"All right, Napoleon. If you aren't hiding your school report inside your jacket, then take your hand out of there and prove it!"

The mother of **David Livingstone**

"Look Dave, you may imagine that there are gloomier places, but just start by bringing some light to Darkest Glasgow!"

The mother of **Isaac Newton**

"Don't lie to me, 'Zac; apples don't simply fall off trees by themselves."

The mother of **Albert Einstein**

"Look, Bert, stop fiddling with equations and just learn your multiplication tables."

The mother of **Thomas Edison**

"Tom, of course I'm proud that you invented the electric light bulb. Now turn off that light and get to bed!"

The mother of **Charles Dawin**

"Charlie boy, just take the dog for a walk, she's more intelligent than any of the zoo animals. Spend any more time there and you'll behave like an ape!"

The mother of **Alexander Flemming**

"Alex, I'm not telling you again. If you don't wash your neck you will start to grow mould behind your ears."

Pay attention to your father, and don't neglect your mother when she grows old. Invest in truth and wisdom, discipline and good sense, and don't part with them. Make your father truly happy by living right and showing sound judgment. Make your parents proud, especially your mother.

Proverbs 23:22-25 (CEV)

Seniors can Think Positively

"Dance Bertha, dance"

This was written by an eighty-three-year-old woman to her friend!

Dear Bertha,

I'm enjoying more and fretting less. I'm reading more and dusting less. I have pulled out some of my favourite old books and revelled in the old stories and poems. I'm sitting in the garden and admiring the view without fussing too much about the weeds. I'm using things more and not bothering to display them. I've taken out the 'best wedding china' with its lovely decorations and gilt. I think they're exquisite, but the family despises fancy crockery. I'm burning the gift candles. I'm sharing more and hoarding less. I've taken the family to the expensive musical extravaganza and enjoyed the company and the show.

Whenever possible, life should be a pattern of experiences to enjoy, not to endure. I'm trying to recognize every good moment and cherish it. I'm not saving anything. I'm using my smartest clothes. I wear my best coat to the market. My theory is, if I look prosperous, I can afford to fork out £14.20 for the bag of groceries. I'm not saving my good perfume for special parties but wearing it for the lady in the next seat in the bus or the checkout workers at the supermarket.

"Someday I'll" and "one of these days" are losing their grip on my vocabulary. If it's worth seeing or hearing or doing, I want to see and hear and do it now. What would our croaked friends have done if they knew they wouldn't be here for the tomorrow that we all take for granted? I think they would have called the family and a few close friends. They might have called a few former friends to apologize and mend fences for past squabbles. I think they would have gone out for a special dinner or to savour their favourite food. I'm guessing; I'll never know.

If I knew my hours were limited, and of course they are, it's those little things left undone that would make me angry. Angry because I hadn't written certain letters that I intended to write "one of these days". Angry and sorry that I didn't tell my husband and parents often enough how much I truly love them. I'm trying hard not to put off or hold back anything that would add laughter and lustre to our lives. And every morning when I open my eyes, I tell myself that it is special. Every day, every minute, every breath truly is a gift from God.

So there it is, Bertha, life may not be the party we hoped for, but while we are here we should surely dance. Indeed, we've been invited to dance – so dance, Bertha, dance!

Love, Mavis.

DANCE BERTHA

Dancing, an oft' neglected medium of worship

David was dancing before the LORD with all his might.

2 Samuel 6:14 (NIV)

Probably many Seniors sympathise with David's wife. She thought that this lacked decorum and was undignified exhibitionism. But David was "dancing for the Lord".

Here are three songs or poems. Can you find the music to sing and dance to?

Growing Old

When the body crumbles
And no longer answers
To my wit or desire

When my fingers can no longer work
Nor eyes see stitches in
The tapestry I wish to make

When limbs creak and stiffen
And skin shrivels with age
And breath comes slowly

Then, Lord, in my dependence
Light a fire within my heart
To set ablaze my inner life

To leap and dance
        at your creation's tune.
For the spirit's freedom
        and the world's gain.

Author unknown

Teach Me to Dance

Teach me to dance to the beat of your heart,
Teach me to move in the pow'r of your Spirit,
Teach me to trust in the word of your promise,
Teach me to hope in the day of your coming,
Teach me to dance to the beat of your heart.

You wrote the rhythm of life,
created heaven and earth,
in you is joy without measure.
So, like a child in your sight,
I dance to see your delight,
for I was made for your pleasure,
    pleasure.

Let all my movements express
a heart that loves to say "yes",
a will that leaps to obey you.
Let all my energy blaze,
to see the joy in your face;
let my whole being praise you,
    praise you.

Graham Kendrick and Steve Thompson
© 1993 Make Way Music.
www.grahamkendrick.co.uk

Lord of the Dance

I danced in the morning
    when the world was begun,
And I danced in the moon
    and the stars and the sun,
I came down from heaven
    and I danced on the earth;
At Bethlehem I had my birth.

Refrain:
Dance, then, wherever you may be;
I am the Lord of the Dance, said he,
And I'll lead you all, wherever you may be,
And I'll lead you all in the dance, said he.

I danced for the scribe and the pharisee,
But they would not dance
    and they would not follow me.
I danced for the fishermen, for James and John
They came with me and the dance went on.

Refrain

I danced on the Sabbath and I cured the lame;
The holy people said it was a shame.
They whipped and they stripped
    and they hung me on high;
They left me there on a cross to die.

Refrain

I danced on a Friday when the sky turned black
It's hard to dance with the devil on your back.
They buried my body and they thought I'd gone;
But I am the dance and I still go on.

Refrain

They cut me down and I leapt up high;
I am the life that will never, never die;
I'll live in you if you'll live in me
I am the Lord of the Dance, said he.

Refrain

Sydney Carter

111

Seniors Against Impersonal Service[11]

Dear Sir,

I am writing to thank you for bouncing my cheque with which I endeavoured to pay my plumber last month. By my calculations, three nanoseconds must have elapsed between his presenting the cheque and the arrival in my account of the funds needed to honour it. I refer to the automatic monthly deposit of my entire pension, an arrangement which, I admit, has been in place for only eight years. I commend you for seizing that brief window of opportunity, and debiting my account $30 by way of penalty for the inconvenience caused to your bank.

My thankfulness springs from the manner in which this incident has caused me to rethink my errant financial ways. I noticed that whereas I personally answer your telephone calls and letters, when I try to contact you, I am confronted by the impersonal, overcharging, pre-recorded, faceless entity which your bank has become.

From now on, I, like you, choose only to deal with a flesh-and-blood person. My mortgage and loan

---

[11] Modified from a true letter from an eighty-six-year-old lady to her Bank Manager

repayments will therefore and hereafter no longer be automatic, but will arrive at your bank, by cheque, addressed personally and confidentially to an employee at your bank whom you must nominate. Be aware that it is an offense under the Postal Act for any other person to open such an envelope. Please find attached an Application Contract which I require your chosen employee to complete. I am sorry it runs to eight pages, but in order that I know as much about him or her as your bank knows about me, there is no alternative.

Please note that all copies of his or her medical history must be countersigned by a Notary Public, and the mandatory details of his/her financial situation (income, debts, assets and liabilities) must be accompanied by documented proof.

In due course, at **my** convenience, I will issue your employee with a PIN number which he/she must quote in dealings with me. I regret that it cannot be shorter than 28 digits but, again, I have modelled it on the number of button presses required of me to access my account balance on your phone bank service. They say, imitation is the sincerest form of flattery.

Let me level the playing field even further. When you call me, press buttons as follows:

Immediately after dialling, press the star (*) button for English, then...

#1. To make an appointment to see me.

#2. To query a missing payment.

#3. To transfer the call to my living room in case I am there.

#4. To transfer the call to my bedroom in case I am sleeping.

#5. To transfer the call to my toilet in case I am attending to nature.

#6. To transfer the call to my mobile phone if I am not at home.

#7. To leave a message on my computer. A password to access my computer is required. The password will be communicated later to that Authorized Contact mentioned earlier.

#8. To return to the main menu and to listen to options 1 through 7.

#9. To make a general complaint or inquiry. The contact will then be put on hold, pending the attention of my automated answering service.

#0. If you require a cooling off period to consider this transaction.

While this may, on occasion, involve a lengthy wait, Beethoven's 9th Symphony, 'Ode to Joy', will play for the duration of the delay.

Regrettably, but again following your example, I must also levy an establishment fee to cover the setting up of this new arrangement.

May I wish you a happy, if ever so slightly less prosperous, New Year.

Your Humble Client.

P.S. And remember, don't make Senior clients mad. They don't like being old in the first place, so it doesn't take much to set us off. They have some experience and know a good service from a bad one. It is now much easier to switch banks!

The Bank Manager thought it was amusing enough to publish it in the New York Times. More important, the bank has subsequently changed its practice when dealing with Senior clients. Many banks, insurance companies, etc. must take cognizance.

Seniors Respond with Wit and Wisdom

Be prepared for any 'put downs'.

Lady Astor: "If you were my husband, I'd give you poison."

Churchill: "If you were my wife, I'd drink it."

MP: "Sir, you will either die on the gallows or of some unspeakable disease."

Disraeli: "That depends, Sir, whether I embrace your policies or your mistress."

"He had delusions of adequacy."

Walter Kerr

"He has all the virtues I dislike and none of the vices I admire."

Winston Churchill

"I have never killed a man, but I have read many obituaries with great pleasure."

Clarence Darrow

"I didn't attend the funeral, but I sent a nice letter saying I approved of it."

Mark Twain

"He has no enemies, but is intensely disliked by his friends."

Oscar Wilde

"He has never been known to use a word that might send a reader to the dictionary."

William Faulkner
About Ernest Hemingway

"Thank you for sending me a copy of your book; I'll waste no time reading it."

Moses Hadas

George Bernard Shaw: "I am enclosing two tickets to the first night of my new play; bring a friend.... if you have one."

Winston Churchill: "Cannot possibly attend first night, will attend second... if there is one."

"I feel so miserable without you; it's almost like having you here."

Stephen Bishop

"He is a self-made man and worships his creator."

John Bright

"He loves nature in spite of what it did to him."

Forrest Tucker

"I've just learned about his illness. Let's hope it's nothing trivial."

Irvin S. Cobb

"He is not only dull himself; he is the cause of dullness in others."

Samuel Johnson

"He is simply a shiver looking for a spine to run up."

Paul Keating

"Why do you sit there looking like an envelope without any address on it?"

Mark Twain

"His mother should have thrown him away and kept the stork."

Mae West

"Some cause happiness wherever they go; others, whenever they go."

Oscar Wilde

"He uses statistics as a drunken man uses lamp-posts – for support rather than illumination."

Andrew Lang (1844-1912)

"I've had a perfectly wonderful evening. But this wasn't it."

Groucho Marx

"He has Van Gogh's ear for music."

Billy Wilder

Seniors – Help Protect the Planet

Ghillean Prance[12] is a world famous plant specialist and campaigner for the environment. After twenty-five years as Director of Economic Botany at the New York Botanical Garden and much field research in Amazonia, he became director of the Royal Botanic Gardens in Kew, London. Now, as Sir Ghillean, he is Director of the Eden Project in Cornwall, and leader of A Rocha conservation group.

He believes strongly that men and women today should accept God's command to work at and care for the world and its plants and animals.

> The LORD God took the man and put him in the Garden of Eden to work it and take care of it.
>
> *Genesis 2:15 (NIV)*

Sir Ghillean declares that as a result of his research findings, he would like to add further verses to the awe-inspiring list of wonders of creation described in Psalm 104. Here are just four verses, but open your Bible and see the splendour of the whole Psalm.

> He waters the mountains from his upper chambers; the land is satisfied by the fruit of his work. He makes grass grow for the cattle, and plants for people to cultivate – bringing forth food from the earth: wine that gladdens human hearts, oil to make their faces shine, and bread

---

[12] See 'Real Science, Real Faith'; Monarch Publications (1991): ISBN:1-85424-125-7

that sustains their hearts. The trees of the LORD are well watered, the cedars of Lebanon that he planted.

Psalm 104:13-16 (NIV)

During his many visits to Amazonian Brazil, Prance was horrified at the destruction of the rainforests, which he considers an ecological disaster. The tropical rainforests cover just 2% of the Earth's land surface, but they are home to two-thirds of all the living species on the planet. A hectare (2.5 acres) of rainforest absorbs one ton of carbon dioxide (CO_2) per year. But the rainforest is being destroyed at the rate of 1.5 acres every second. That is the equivalent of two football fields. At the present rate half of all rainforest will be gone by 2025, and it will all be gone by 2060! Ghillean Prance believes that Christians who know and worship the Creator God, rather than just the creation, should be at the forefront of environmental protection.

Seniors, especially those of us born in the first half of the Twentieth Century, already know about conservation. We lived through the austerities from World War 2. We remember food rationing and hate to see people overload their plates and then leave much food. Many abhor the current extravagant excesses and the wasteful lifestyles of rich people, especially in the industrialised world. During the World War, we used to save everything that could be reused, and when food was short, every small plot became a productive garden. Unnecessary growth of consumption must stop if the planet is to survive!

Conservation is a huge and important topic.[13] These issues are a challenge for all of us.

Prayer

Dear Father God, we thank you for this world.

We wonder at the incredible and intricate detail, from sub-microscopic genes to the laws of thermodynamics that fine-balance infinite factors to enable life to continue.

We wonder at the amazing colours and beauty of multiple forms of life, including human beings made in your image and able to think, reason and appreciate moral laws.

Father, forgive us that with your gift of free will, we plunder and pillage the resources of the earth for short-term satisfaction. Forgive us that we selfishly store and protect even essentials like food while others go hungry.

Dear Father God, make us sensitive to the big environmental issues. Give us wisdom to judge what we need to do to correct the consumption explosion and exploitation of the earth.

Father God, give us determination to play our part and encourage others to care more for your creation and share more of what you have given us.

Amen.

---

[13] See page 131

The Creator is worried – with good reason!

"Where have all the flowers gone?"

Apologies to Pete Seeger, 1955!

GOD:

Frank, you know all about gardens and nature.
What in the world is going on down there on the
planet? What happened to the daisies, dandelions,
violets, milkweeds and stuff that I started eons
ago? I had a perfect no-maintenance garden plan.
Those plants grow in any type of soil, withstand
drought and multiply with abandon. The nectar

from the long-lasting blossoms attracts butterflies, honey bees and flocks of songbirds. I expected to see a vast garden of colours by now. But, all I see are these green rectangles. What's going on?

ST. FRANCIS:

It's the tribes that settled there, Lord. The Suburbanites, they started calling your flowers 'weeds' and went to great lengths to kill them and replace them with grass.

GOD:

Grass? But, it's so boring. It's not colourful. It doesn't attract butterflies, birds and bees; only grubs and sod worms. It's sensitive to temperatures. Do these Suburbanites really want all that grass growing there?

ST. FRANCIS:

Apparently so, Lord. They go to great pains to grow it and keep it green. They begin each spring by fertilizing grass and poisoning any other plant that crops up in the lawn.

GOD:

The spring rains and warm weather probably make grass grow really fast. That must make the Suburbanites happy.

ST. FRANCIS:

Apparently not, Lord. As soon as it grows a little, they cut it, sometimes twice a week.

GOD:

They cut it? Do they then bale it like hay?

ST. FRANCIS:

Not exactly, Lord. Most of them rake it up and put it in bags.

GOD:

They bag it? Why? Is it a cash crop? Do they sell it?

ST. FRANCIS:

No, Sir, just the opposite. They pay to throw it away.

GOD:

Now, let me get this straight. They fertilize grass so it will grow. And, when it does grow, they cut it off and pay to throw it away?

ST. FRANCIS:

Yes, Sir.

GOD:

These Suburbanites must be relieved in the summer when we cut back on the rain and turn up the heat. That surely slows the growth and saves them a lot of work.

ST. FRANCIS:

You aren't going to believe this, Lord. When the grass stops growing so fast, they drag out hoses and pay more money to water it, so they can continue to mow it and pay to get rid of it.

GOD:

What nonsense! At least they kept some of the trees. That was a sheer stroke of genius, if I do say so myself. The trees grow leaves in the spring to provide beauty and shade in the summer. In the autumn, they fall to the ground and form a natural blanket to keep moisture in the soil and protect the trees and bushes. It's a natural cycle of life.

ST. FRANCIS:

You better sit down, Lord. The Suburbanites have drawn a new cycle. As soon as the leaves fall, they rake them into great piles and pay to have them hauled away.

GOD:

No!? What do they do to protect the shrub and tree roots in the winter to keep the soil moist and loose?

ST. FRANCIS:

After throwing away the leaves, they go out and buy something which they call mulch. They haul it home and spread it around in place of the leaves.

GOD:

And where do they get this mulch?

ST. FRANCIS:

They cut down trees and grind them up to make the mulch.

GOD:

Enough! I don't want to think about this anymore. St. Catherine, you're in charge of the arts. What movie have you scheduled for us tonight?

ST. CATHERINE:

A comedy from Planet Earth, Lord. 'Dumb and Dumber'. It's a story about…

GOD:

Never mind, I think I just heard the whole story from St. Francis.

A Senior Lifestyle that Doesn't Cost the Earth

Seniors can lead on conservation and planet protection

Seniors, we all know that human dependence on fossil fuels is not sustainable, and burning them in increasing amounts has a measurable and very probable dangerous effect on the global climate.[14]

Moreover, I believe that God created the world, loves it and has given each one of us the privilege of looking after it. This involves many areas of our lives, from our own day-to-day choices at home, in the shops, as we travel, and also as we campaign about what happens nationally and internationally. We need to think globally but act locally and personally. The church must recover its ecological conscience and seize the opportunities to make Jesus known as Lord by caring for his creation. Seniors can take a responsible lead.

Unfortunately, politicians, financiers and manufacturers all have the objective of 'growth' and do not consider the alternative or that some resources in the planet are finite and within a few generations some materials will be exhausted. Sharing what we have and caring for the world would seem

---

[14] 'Sustainable energy without hot air' by David J. C. Mackay (downloadable from *www.withouthotair.com/download.html*).
"At last a book that comprehensively reveals the true facts about sustainable energy in a form that is both highly readable and entertaining." – Robert Sansom (EDF Energy).

to be the fair and just way forward to respect people and protect the beautiful, God-given planet.

Responsible Seniors want to be more planet-friendly. The number and nature of possible interventions is great. Individuals need to choose for themselves which are the most feasible and effective actions that they can take. What we do, or do not do, will influence our children and their children for future generations.

Food

Food is essential and enjoyable, but its production and distribution has the biggest environmental impact. The U.N. Food and Agriculture Organisation (FAO) stated that "meat and dairy production contribute more to climate change than the entire global transport sector (18% versus 13.5%)." Even if the calculations are disputed by some, these animal products have a massive impact on the environment.

The vegan/vegetarian/meat-eating debate is complicated and must be approached with graciousness on all sides. You can start simply by eating meat less often, or eat smaller portions with more vegetables. The second issue is pesticides; the heavy use of these seriously affects wildlife and biodiversity. The third issue is transportation, processing and packaging. These account for 75% of the cost of food. The fourth factor is the welfare of farmed animals or factory farming. The fifth factor is financial power. Big farming is sometimes linked to multinational companies, the use of specific crops (sometimes GM), fertiliser and pesticides, and to the supermarket chains. We must shop, cook and eat responsibly if we are to protect our planet for the future.

- **Give thanks** to God before eating. Try to imagine the places and people who have prepared what you eat. Remember those who will be hungry today.
- Living responsibly may begin by eating more healthily. **Eat less, waste less,** and **cook from real ingredients.**
- If possible, **eat local produce** and **seasonal foods.** Best of all, **grow your own** where you can.

Eating more ethically can seem challenging, so start small and start simple. Good food is a celebration of God's creation and human creativity. Remember that every mouthful is a gift of God's grace, and your body is a temple of God's Spirit (1 Corinthians 6.19). Whatever you do, don't stop enjoying and celebrating the goodness of food!

House

Of the potentially damaging carbon dioxide (CO_2) we produce, a large part comes from energy used to heat (or cool) our homes. Insulation and draft exclusion are important but not easy in older houses. There are some relatively simple ways to limit energy and heat loss, keep your home comfortable, and restrict damage to the environment.

- Look at what can be done with **lightweight insulation materials,** e.g. multi-use foil with and without polystyrene backing; expanded polystyrene boards and polystyrene foam. Their effectiveness depends on the space and budget available.

- **Close internal doors** and **fit draught excluder tape** to both internal and external door frames, and **use curtains** to keep heat in at night. **Fill cracks and gaps** with filler or putty to block out draughts, particularly in ceilings. Thick **loft insulation** is valuable but not always easy to install.

- Go for a **condensing boiler** if possible or put an **insulating jacket** around your hot water tank.

- Fit **heat deflectors** (simple aluminium foil) behind radiators against outside walls to retain heat in your living rooms. **Don't heat the whole house.**

- In his detailed analysis Professor David Mackay admits that probably the most effective way to reduce fuel use is to **turn down the thermostat** and **wear more clothes** indoors.[15]

- In the kitchen, **only boil as much hot water as you need immediately** in your electric kettle.

- Remember that **manufacturing also produces a lot of carbon dioxide.** All new products, even energy-saving devices, produce CO_2 during manufacture and distribution.

---

[15] Ibid.

Waste

In God's creation nothing is wasted: autumn leaves become spring's fertile mulch; every part of creation has a fruitful role to play.

Learn the waste hierarchy –

1. reduce
2. re-use
3. recycle

– and start living by it!

The idea is that it's best to reduce – buy less in the first place and reduce your ecological footprint. Next best is to re-use. And then recycling is the final option.

- **Try to repair** rather than replace things when they break.
- In the UK we each used to throw away an average ½ tonne per year, but now many local councils help by making weekly collections of a range of materials for **recycling**: paper, cardboard, tin cans, plastic and glass bottles. Ask them if they could do more.
- **Use food waste** for compost and **'grey water'** to water your plants.
- **Challenge your supermarket** to use more recyclable containers. Any remaining waste is ultimately a failure of us, or of our culture, to use God's world sustainably.

Tackling waste is not just a technical exercise, but a spiritual discipline. Every bin-bag we thoughtlessly discard is an offering to the idols of consumerism. In contrast, every act that reduces our waste can be an act of worship.

Garden

- **Be creative with your garden,** share it with children, and when they visit do a nature explore, no matter how small your plot is.
- **Eat in the garden** when the weather permits. Some have an area in the garden to meditate.
- **Use a compost heap** and do not use peat-based compost.
- **Avoid pesticides** if possible.
- **Harvest rain water** off the roof into butts and use a watering can rather than a hose.
- **Grow some vegetables** in your garden or even in a window box. Herbs don't take much space. Grow some potatoes, in a big bucket if necessary.
- **Make your garden wildlife-friendly** with bird feeders, water and nesting boxes.
- **Plant some bulbs** on the verges outside your garden.
- **Be a Guerrilla gardener** (clandestine gardening of roundabouts, etc.)

Shopping

Everything we buy has an impact on the environment. The developed countries – only 20% of the world population – are consuming over 80% of the earth's natural resources.

This is an unfair distribution, causing wrong expectations in poorer countries and a disproportionate level of environmental damage.

In a materialist culture we can easily be squeezed into believing that we are what we wear, that our possessions define us, that our happiness depends on spending, replacing, consuming. Living lightly means breaking free from the addiction to consumerism. It is about being a true radical – going back to the roots of what really matters.

- Try to resist the advertisers' pressure, and **buy only what you need,** but don't be afraid to spend well for quality, durability, sustainability and justice.
- If something breaks or tears, **fix and repair** it rather than replace it.
- **Consider the background of each item you buy.** When shopping, remember that every 'thing' comes from somewhere, and was made by someone. What is its story? What materials have been used? In what conditions was it made? How far has it travelled? What wildlife or peoples have been affected? Is it an altruistic dream to minimize the impact of any purchase you make and maximize its benefit to others and the environment?
- Think how you can strike a blow against the environmental and unethical consequences of consumerism. Celebrate a 'Buy Nothing Day' or use Lent to carry out a **shopping fast;** don't buy any stuff other than food and essentials.

- Take your unwanted clothes and goods to **charity shops**.
- Set up your own version of **'Freecycle'** at church, school, office, giving people the opportunity both to pass on things that they no longer need and to request things that they do need.

Travel

Travel is important for Seniors. It brings freedoms, and lets families get together; air-miles are sometimes love-miles. But travel and transport can also damage the planet and the people who live on it.

- Consider the opportunity to **travel less** and get to know better the people and the place where God has planted you.
- When you do have to travel try to **pollute less** and compensate through climate stewardship.
- **Walk or cycle** for all shorter journeys.
- **Use public transport** as much as possible. Seniors, use your free or concessional travel with gratitude, imagination and joy.
- **Share your car** with other people and another family as often as possible.
- Try a week of **'car fasting'**.
- **Slow down.** Driving at 50mph takes about 25-30% less fuel than at 70mph. Accelerate and brake gently.
- If you are changing cars, go **eco-friendly**.

Concluding challenge

What lifestyle changes are you and I willing to make, using a little technology where necessary, to reduce the damage that humans are doing to the planet and its environment? Seniors must set an example of lifestyle changes to limit excessive consumption and waste. We must each shrink our personal 'carbon footprint'.

Based on ideas from Ruth Valerio[16] and John Rankin

Further Information

'A Rocha'[17] is an international Christian organization which, inspired by God's love, engages in scientific research, environmental education and community-based conservation projects.

> "We believe that there is hope, and we can all make a difference, with some help from our friends. Its vision is the transformation of people and places, as individuals and communities do their bit to care for God's world."

---

[16] *www.lisforlifestyle.com* and *'L' is for Lifestyle: Christian Living That Doesn't Cost the Earth;* IVP (2008)
[17] *www.arocha.org/int-en*

Seniors, the True Green Generation

When we were young there was less danger to the planet.

At the checkout in the supermarket, the young cashier told the Senior shopper that she must bring her own bags for her groceries because plastic bags weren't good for the environment.

The Senior lady apologized to her and explained, "We didn't have 'the green thing' back in my young days."

The young cashier responded, "That's the problem you old folks have landed on us. Your generation did not care enough to save our environment."

Then the Senior lady thought about it.

"In the past, we returned milk bottles, soft drink bottles and beer bottles to the shop. The shop sent them back to the factory to be washed and sterilized and refilled, so it could use the same bottles over and over. Bottles and many other things were recycled or stored for future use. That's True Green!"

She thought again.

"Those days most children got hand-down and home-repaired clothes from their brothers, sisters or cousins. Brand-new clothes were only for special occasion. Also, kids made a few pennies pocket money by selling all the old newspapers to the fish-and-chip shop for wrapping. That was True Green. But now the fish and chips must be wrapped in hygienic white paper and put in cardboard boxes.

"Plastic bags were not thought of in my young days. The groceries were repacked in used cardboard boxes kept in the stores. But now they are flattened in a big power press out the back of the supermarket. Back then, we didn't fire up a petrol motor and burn fuel or electricity just to cut the lawn. We used a push mower that ran on human power. We used hand sheers to trim the hedges. We were True Green.

"When we were thirsty, we drank a glass of water filled from the tap. We never used a plastic bottle every time we had a drink and then threw it away and bought another. We re-filled our writing pens with ink instead of buying a new pen. My Dad had the same razor all his life. When a blade became blunt he would change the razor-blade, not simply throw the whole razor away! We were True Green then.

"Back then, we had one radio and later one TV in the house, not one in every room. And the TV had a small screen the size of a handkerchief, not a huge screen the size of the wall. In the kitchen, we blended, stirred and chopped by hand because we didn't have electric machines to do everything. To get my oven clean I did not use electric power and a special 'oven cleaning cycle', but the job was done with some Vim and elbow grease.

"Think of batteries: in the old days these we used these in torches or flashlights, but now every house needs dozens of batteries for mobile phones, computers and toys. Even salt cellars and pepper grinders depend on batteries rather than shake-power, which was True Green.

"In our homes back then we had one electrical outlet in a room, not an entire bank of sockets to power a dozen appliances. Few homes had central heating; we worked around the house and wore an extra jersey to keep warm. Now many keep their houses heated to tropical temperatures. Air conditioning in a house was unknown, but people opened their windows and let in the fresh breeze. That was True Green.

"In those days we walked up stairs because they didn't have a lift or an escalator in every store and office building. We also walked to the grocer's shop and didn't climb into a two hundred horsepower machine every time we wanted to visit someone a couple of streets away. People walked or took the bus, and kids rode their bikes to school or went in the school bus instead of turning their mums into a twenty-four-hour taxi service. We exercised by walking to work and doing physical jobs so we didn't need to go to a gym or a costly health club to run on treadmills that operate on electricity. We lived True Green.

"When we packaged a fragile item to send it by post, we scrumpled newspaper to cushion it. Later, the paper was so easily biodegradable, unlike the plastic bubble wrap or polystyrene styrofoam. When we went on holiday we did not jet off in a plane that damages the ozone layer; we hiked around the countryside, swam in the rivers and lakes, and enjoyed the fresh air. In the old days we were True Green.

"Oh yes, the washing. We washed the baby's nappies (diapers) because we didn't have the throw-away kind. Then we dried clothes on a line in the back garden, not in a powerful energy-gobbling tumble dryer. Guess what? Clothes were dried by wind power and solar energy! How green is that! In those days we lived frugally and were careful with everything."

We Seniors are the real eco-friendly, the True Green generation!

Dust if You Must!

Dust if you must, but wouldn't it be better
To paint a picture, or write a letter,
Bake a cake, or plant a seed;
Ponder the difference between want and need?

Dust if you must, but there's not much time,
With rivers to swim, and mountains to climb;
Music to hear, and books to read;
Friends to cherish, and life to lead.

Dust if you must, but the world's out there
With the sun in your eyes,
    and the wind in your hair;
A flutter of snow, a shower of rain,
This day will not come around again.

Dust if you must, but time's passing much faster.
I must do my bit against cosmic disaster.
While science and politics argue the toss,
I'll walk to shops and limit the loss.

Dust if you must, but just bear in mind,
Old age will come and it is not kind.
And when you go, and go you must,
You, yourself, will make more dust.

Remember, a house becomes a home when you can write "I love you" on the furniture…

Seniors

can model values

Face the Future

Seniors can Show Patience

A woman in a supermarket follows a grandfather and his badly behaved three-year-old grandson. It's obvious to her that he has his hands full with the child screaming for sweets in the sweet aisle, biscuits in the biscuit aisle, and for fruit, cereal and drinks in the other aisles.

Meanwhile, Grandpa is working his way around, saying in a controlled voice, "Easy, Jonathan, we won't be long... Easy, boy!" Another outburst, and she hears the granddad calmly say, "It's okay, Jonathan, just a couple more minutes and we'll be out of here. Hang in there, boy."

At the checkout, the little terror is throwing items out of the trolley-cart, and Grandpa says again in a controlled voice, "Jonathan, Jonathan, relax buddy. Don't get upset! We'll be home in ten minutes. Stay cool, Jonathan!"

Very impressed, the woman goes outside where the grandfather is loading his groceries and the boy into the car.

She says to the elderly gentleman, "It's none of my business, but you were amazing in there. I don't know how you did it. That whole time, you kept your composure, and no matter how loud and disruptive he got, you just calmly kept saying things would be okay. Jonathan is very lucky to have such a patient Grandpa."

"Thanks, lady," said the grandfather. "Long ago I learnt from my own Dad what to do when patience and calm encouragement are required. By the way, the name of the little terror is Tony. *I'm* Jonathan."

We live in a society which is impatient for what it wants. It encourages instant gratification. The banks developed credit cards so you could get what you wanted immediately. The slogan of one card was "It takes the waiting out of wanting". But what you have obtained with your card may be worn out before you have paid for it. This attitude has resulted in the debts into which individuals, banks and even nations have fallen. This attitude is the very opposite of patience.

Paul, the missionary apostle, wrote to the young churches in southern Turkey about twenty years after Jesus died and rose. He wrote to encourage faith and freedom in Jesus. He compared selfish and bad thoughts and actions with the sort of good thoughts, deeds and virtues that should develop if God's Spirit dwelt in the hearts of believers. These good attributes Paul called the Fruit of the Spirit.

> But the fruit of the Spirit is love, joy, peace, patience, kindness, goodness, faithfulness, gentleness and self-control. Against such things there is no law.
>
> *Galatians 5:22-23 (NIV)*

Right in the middle of that impressive list is **patience**. It is a fruit that sometimes takes a long time to ripen, sometimes most of a lifetime! It is something many Seniors know about because it may develop, often over years, from disappointments, hardships and struggles.

Seniors, strengthen your patience with these thoughts and check the references:

- We can be patient because we know that God often uses trials, disappointments and suffering for our growth and our good. (2 Thessalonians 1:4)
- Patience and persistence go together. We need to be faithfully diligent and keep working at things. Any great carving is created by chipping away, a flake at a time.
- Patience is an active, not a passive, virtue. "Run with patience the race..." (Hebrews 12:1, KJV). 'Patience' is translated 'endurance' and 'perseverance' in modern translations. You are competing not observing. You must work at it! That is what Granddad Jonathan demonstrated.
- We can wait patiently without worry because we know who is at the controls. Impatience is wanting to be in control. It comes from not wanting to give power to someone else, not admitting that there is a powerful God who is in the driver's seat. Move over and let Him drive!
- We know that the ultimate future is secure; it is in God's hands. He has promised that. Short term things seem to go wrong, there may be frustrations and difficulties, but we believe His promise and trust that God is working for our good in all things. (Romans 8:28)

The devout young man prayed, "Lord, I want patience, and I want it right **now!**" He needs it!

Prayer

Thank you, Lord, for being patient with me when I'm slow to respond to your love.

Lord, make me persistent in my endeavours and patient in my trials because I trust in your love.

Amen.

New Definition for S.O.S.

A C-130 (Hercules, heavy transport plane) was lumbering along when a cocky F-16 (fighter plane) flashed by.

The fighter pilot decided to show off.

The fighter jock told the C-130 pilot, "Watch this!" and promptly went into a barrel roll followed by a steep climb. He then finished with a sonic boom as he broke the sound barrier.

The F-16 pilot asked the C-130 transport pilot what he thought of that.

The C-130 pilot said, "That was impressive, but watch this!"

The C-130 droned along for about five minutes and then the C-130 pilot came back on and said, "What did you think of that?"

Puzzled, the F-16 pilot asked, "What the heck did you do?"

The C-130 pilot chuckled. "I stood up, stretched my legs, walked to the back, visited the comfort room, then got a cup of coffee and a cinnamon roll."

When you are young and foolish, speed and flash may seem a good thing! When you get older and smarter, comfort and reliability is not such a bad thing!

We older folks understand this one.

It's called S.O.S.: Slower, Older and Smarter...

Seniors can Model Loving Care

It was a busy morning, about 8:30 am, when an elderly gentleman, in his eighties, fresh-shaven and tidy, presented at the Emergency Department to have sutures (stitches) removed from his hand. He said that he was in a hurry as he had an appointment at 9:00 am.

I, the nurse, took his vital signs, temperature, pulse and respiratory rate. They were fine and I asked him to take a seat, knowing it would be over an hour before someone would be able to attend to him.

I saw him looking at his watch and decided, since I was not too busy with another patient, I would check his wound. On examination it was well healed, so I talked to one of the doctors and collected the necessary supplies to remove his sutures and redress his wound.

While taking care of his wound, we began to talk. I asked him if he had a doctor's appointment this morning somewhere else, as he was in such a hurry. The gentleman told me, no, that he needed to go to the nursing home to eat breakfast and help with his wife. I then enquired about her health. He told me that she had been there for some years and that she had severe Alzheimer's Disease.

As we talked, and I finished dressing his wound, I asked if she would be worried if he was a bit late. He replied that she no longer knew who he was, that she had not recognized him in five years now.

I was surprised, and asked him, "And you are still going every morning, even though she doesn't know who you are?"

He smiled as he thanked me and patted my hand. "She doesn't know me, but I still know who she is!"

I had to hold back tears as he left and thought, "That is the kind of love I want in my life."

Dick Fincham

Here is another similar story.

Dick was over ninety when we first met him. He was significantly disabled, having had a partial stroke, but he was full of vitality. He never ceased to tell his friends that the two greatest things in his life were his marriage to Ruby and his coming to faith in Jesus Christ. He was constantly amazed and thankful for these two wonders in his life. He was a good raconteur, easy to listen to, with an amazing memory for detail. But in all his conversations and all his stories he would circle back to these two life-changing events.

Dick loved to think of himself as a restaurateur and caterer, but he admits that after the first day that he took over their first little business he was in dire trouble.

"Ruby, please will you come and help me by running the kitchen, just for a few days."

She must have had a flare for both the cooking and managing of the small staff, and I think that she ran the kitchen for the rest of her working life. Their most famous establishment was 'Queen's Fare' in Richmond-on-Thames, and apparently it was such a success that there was usually a queue outside for the lunches.

For the last twenty years of her life, Ruby became progressively more disabled, first blind and then with dementia, complicated by a serious head injury. During all this time, and especially in her last ten years, she probably did not know who was looking after her, but Dick cared for her hand and foot, feeding and toileting her, though she could not even speak or respond. He did this day after day, week after week, month after month for years. Dick was far from well himself, seriously limited by his stroke and other ailments, but these things did not stop him from his caring and from taking an interest in his family and other people. But above all Dick loved Ruby deeply, until she died – and afterwards. He still missed her greatly and spoke of her every single time we saw him.

True love is much more than physical or romantic. True love includes an acceptance of all that is, all that has been, and all that will be and will not be. Where does such love come from? Dick was certain that this comes from God himself. Agape love is the love of God in Christ for mankind. It is unconditional, active, thoughtful, self-sacrificing love, expecting nothing in return. Saint Paul describes it in his famous letter.

> Love ... is patient, is kind, does not envy, does not boast, is not proud, is not rude, is not self-seeking ... is not easily angered, keeps no records of wrongs, does not delight in evil, but rejoices in truth ... Always

protects, always trusts, always hopes, always perseveres … Love never fails.

1 Corinthians 13:4-8 (NIV)

Paul described it – but Dick lived it.

Prayer

Thank you, Lord Jesus, for your supreme love shown in your life and death.

Thank you for the love demonstrated to men and women during the agonies of your painful death:

- asking forgiveness for those who were killing you;
- showing concern for your mother and commending her to the care of another; and
- promising forgiveness to a repentant criminal who knew he did not deserve it.

Thank you, Lord God, for the simpler examples of selfless love that we have seen in action.

Lord God, give a special gift of this love to all who care for others, especially when those cared for are no longer able to say thank you.

Lord God, grant us all some of this amazing love in our own weak and fickle hearts.

Amen.

Wedding fairy – Be careful what you wish

A married couple in their early sixties were celebrating their fortieth wedding anniversary in a quiet, romantic little restaurant.

Suddenly, a tiny, beautiful fairy appeared on their table.

She said, "I am your Wedding Fairy. For being such an exemplary married couple and for showing love to each other for all this time, I will grant you each a wish."

The wife answered, "Oh, I want to travel around the world with my darling husband."

The fairy waved her magic wand and – *poof!* – two tickets for a round-the-world cruise appeared in her hand.

The husband thought for a moment. "Well, this is all very romantic, but an opportunity like this will never come again. I'm sorry, my love, but for this trip my wish is to have a wife thirty years younger than me."

The wife and the fairy were both disappointed, but a wish is a wish.

"No problem!" said the fairy. She waved her magic wand and – *poof!* – the husband became ninety-two years old.

Note: Actually, Seniors know that **how you live** and **what you feel like** are more important than what you look like!

Seniors can Give Encouragement

Dr David Morley was a world famous Professor of Tropical Child Health in the University of London and used to visit health programmes in Africa and India each year with a group of his international trainees.[18]

In September 1969 he was in Hyderabad, South India. At that time I was working in a small hospital in an impoverished rural area two hundred miles to the south. David had one day off from his duties and he chose to use it to visit us, an unknown team in a remote area. This required two overnight journeys on an uncomfortable local bus over some dreadful and dangerous roads. In the intervening day he dispensed big doses of encouragement that are still remembered years later. He had an infectious enthusiasm which encouraged countless medical and nursing trainees to work in child health services in needy areas. Even in his eighties he was thinking of new ways of giving encouragement to health workers. He used to say, "Look out for what people are doing right and give them praise. You must give three words of encouragement for every one word of correction."

---

[18] David C. Morley (1923-2009)
  Cambridge and St. Thomas' Hospital, London,
  Wesley Guild Hospital, Ilesha, Nigeria 1953-1961,
  London School of Hygiene and Tropical Medicine 1961-1964,
  Institute of Child Health, London 1965-1989.
  Director of Teaching Aids at Low Cost (TALC) 1965-2009.
  See www.talcuk.org.uk

People wonder at the sort of men Jesus chose to be his disciples. Simon, one of the first, was unreliable. He could have been called 'Simon the Shaky'. He repeatedly blurted things out; he was brash and impulsive; he opened his mouth and put his foot in it. He was full of bravado, yet cowardly. Even when Jesus warned him that he would betray him, Peter said, "Never!" – and then disowned his master three times!

But he did have some brilliant insights and recognised Jesus for who he was: "You are the Christ, the Son of the living God." (Matthew 16:16, NIV)

Because of this, Jesus saw the potential in him, encouraged him with generous praise, and said, "I tell you that you are Peter, and on this rock I will build my church." (Matthew 16:18) You are not just Peter the Pebble, but you are 'Petros', Peter the Rock. You are so important that I give you this new name to remember who you are.

His encouragement gave Peter confidence and strength to live up to his potential.

Seniors sometimes look at the rising generations with scorn and are ready with criticism. It is true that many young people now have new opportunities, but these bring different challenges and pressures which previous generations did not have to face. They need confidence and direction. Seniors can help them by looking out for what they do right, admiring the skills they have, and giving them a word of praise and appreciation. So, look out for their potential and give a word of encouragement. This is what Jesus did for Peter and what David Morley did for many.

Remember David's dictum: "Give three doses of praise for every one of correction."

Prayer

Lord God, make me an encourager not a grumbler.

Lord, when I meet someone;

- Open my vision that I may see beyond their limitations to their potential.
- Open my eyes to see in their efforts something well done.
- Open my lips that I may speak a word of praise and encouragement.

Lord, may the youngsters develop into the people that You would have them be.

Amen.

A Royal Senior Models Faithful Service

June 2012 – and Britain gave a right regal and often quirky celebration to Queen Elizabeth on the Diamond Jubilee of her accession to the Throne. No expense was spared, despite the country being officially in 'recession'. From stirring pageantry to soaked street parties, the nation saluted a Queen who has served her people for over sixty years, through her own family troubles and many national and international political changes.

She has seen twelve Prime Ministers come and go.

Politicians and potentates from across the world paid homage and attended banquets, but there were also some simple, touching gestures. A West African schoolgirl who won a scholarship to a British school, and a young man who teaches gardening to young offenders in a London prison, shared a table with Prince William and his Princess Kate.

There was an enormous open-air concert outside Buckingham Palace with famous British and international stars. On the River Thames was the Jubilee Regatta, the largest for over three hundred years, a flotilla of over one thousand vessels. It was impressive... but not spectacular because it was a dreadful day of lowering clouds, chill winds and torrential rain. Hundreds of thousands were drenched, and it was a true test of character and endurance. Tough for the rowers and paddlers, but also for the Queen (eighty-six) and Prince Philip (ninety-one). They stood on deck, waved and saluted for over four hours, non-stop. Was it just an old wives tale that "if you go out inappropriately dressed (fancy, rather than weather-wise) you will catch a chill in your kidneys"? Anyway, poor Prince Philip ended up in hospital with a urinary infection! Not even the greatest monarch of modern times can command the British weather!

Many people, from those interviewed in the street, to the Archbishop of Canterbury in St. Paul's Cathedral, considered the question of the source of Her Majesty's commitment and dedication. She gave a clear, personal testimony in her Christmas broadcast of 2011.

> "Finding hope in adversity is one of the themes of Christmas. Jesus was born into a world full of fear. The angels came to frightened shepherds with hope in their voices: 'Fear not,' they urged, 'we bring you tidings of great joy, which shall be to all people. For unto you is born this day in the City of David a Saviour who is Christ the Lord.' Although we are capable of great acts of kindness, history teaches us that we sometimes need saving from ourselves – from our recklessness or our greed. God sent into the world a unique person – neither a philosopher nor a general, important though they are, but a Saviour, with the power to forgive. Forgiveness lies at the heart of the Christian faith. It can heal broken families, it can restore friendships and it can reconcile divided communities. It is in forgiveness that we feel the

power of God's love. In the last verse of this beautiful carol, 'O Little Town Of Bethlehem', there's a prayer: 'O Holy Child of Bethlehem, descend to us we pray. Cast out our sin and enter in. Be born in us today.' It is my prayer that on this Christmas day we might all find room in our lives for the message of the angels and for the love of God through Christ our Lord."

The Queen: not as well known as she thought![19]

The Queen was visiting a retirement home. She is really good at chatting with all sorts of people, but she was finding conversation with one resident rather difficult. So she asked the elderly lady, "Do you know who I am?"

The old resident replied, "Don't worry about it, my dear. Just ask the nurse when she comes around, and she will tell you."

---

[19] Allegedly a true story about our monarch

Passion: a Potential Force for Good

Sir John Crofton, a passionate, innovative and inspirational physician

In 1952, the year in which John Crofton was appointed Professor of Tuberculosis at the University of Edinburgh (the year in which I joined the medical school there), there were a thousand new cases of tuberculosis (TB) notified in that city of about half a million people. By 1958 (the year in which I graduated) Crofton and his colleagues demonstrated a one hundred per cent cure rate for new TB cases, and control of the disease in the city was in sight.[20]

Many experts were sceptical and flocked to Edinburgh to check the results. This age-old disease, consumption – what John Bunyan (1628-1688), in the 'Pilgrim's Progress' had described as "the captain of the men of death" – was yielding not simply to antimicrobial therapy but to the way it was applied by Crofton and his colleagues. The use of Streptomycin alone was dramatic, but it took months of treatment and the tubercle bacillus readily developed resistance to the drug. Crofton promoted a three-drug regime: Streptomycin with INAH and PAS. If the bacilli became resistant to one medicine, it would be killed by the other two.[21]

---

[20] Holme C.I. "Trial by TB", Proceedings of the Royal College of Physicians of Edinburgh 1997, 27:1

[21] It is no coincidence that antiretroviral therapy against HIV uses multi-drug therapy.

He was truly passionate about multi-drug treatment and the full duration of therapy. In a unique and memorable way he insured that every Edinburgh medical student knew the basic treatment. He said that in the TB exam one question would be compulsory and he would tell us what it was: "What is the correct drug regime and the duration of treatment for someone with TB?" Anyone who failed that question would automatically fail the whole exam.

Sir John Crofton officially 'retired' in 1977, but right up to his death in 2009, three decades later, he was still active and passionate in the fight against chest disease. His battle did not stop with TB. He founded the anti-smoking organisation ASH (Action on Smoking and Health) in Scotland, and when ninety, published his last book, 'Tobacco, a Global Threat'. These have had an important impact, reducing cancer of the lung.

Passion for a great and good cause always deserves commendation. Passion for a good cause that lasts a lifetime, right into the tenth decade, deserves exceptional commendation. Active up to his death at age ninety-seven, John Crofton never retired from being a passionate chest physician. He is an example and encouragement for us all!

Sir John's passion was not motivated by Christian conviction but by humanitarian compassion. But passion is a powerful force. Passion for an evil objective can be horrific. May we never forget the Holocaust! Passion for a good and great cause can also be powerful. It is no coincidence that the last week of Jesus' life on earth is known as 'The Passion'. It started with a crowd of people passionately welcoming him into Jerusalem with cries of "Hosanna!" Jesus then reacted passionately against the abuses in the Temple which had made religious observance into a money market. He also preached stinging criticism against the formal religious leaders. Jesus agonised passionately about doing what God wanted him to do: "Not my will, but yours." That surrender cost him dear. A fickle crowd, stirred up by evil men, reacted passionately against Jesus and shouted, "Crucify him!" and he submitted to a demeaning and dreadful death. But Christians believe that only through that death, and the subsequent resurrection, can come reconciliation to God. Passion for a good cause – the greatest – had eternal consequences.

Prayer

Lord God, may I never be ashamed about being passionate about the important things in life.

Lord God, may I be passionate about poverty and injustice – in the world and in my community.

Lord God, may I love you with all my heart and share that passion with others.

Amen.

Glimpses from Passion Week

JESUS CLEARS THE CROOKS FROM JERUSALEM TEMPLE

They arrived at Jerusalem. Immediately on entering the Temple, Jesus started throwing out everyone who had set up shop there, buying and selling. He kicked over the tables of the bankers and the stalls of the pigeon merchants. He didn't let anyone even carry a basket through the Temple. And then he taught them, quoting this text:

> My house was designated a house of prayer for the nations; you've turned it into a hangout for thieves.
>
> *Mark 11:15-17 (The Message)*

JESUS TEACHING IN THE TEMPLE

He continued teaching.

Watch out for the religious scholars. They love to walk around in academic gowns, preening in the radiance of public flattery, basking in prominent positions, sitting at the head table at every church function. And all the time they are exploiting the weak and helpless. The longer their prayers, the worse they get. But they'll pay for it in the end.

> *Mark 12:38-40 (The Message)*

JESUS PASSIONATELY AGONIZING ABOUT AVOIDING HIS
EXECUTION OR FOLLOWING GOD'S PLAN

> Taking along Peter and the two sons of Zebedee, [Jesus]
> plunged into an agonizing sorrow. Then he said, "This
> sorrow is crushing my life out. Stay here and keep vigil
> with me." Going a little ahead, he fell on his face,
> praying, "My Father, if there is any way, get me out of
> this. But please, not what I want. You, what do you
> want?"
>
> *Matthew 26:38-39*

Seniors can Show Endurance

An endurance exemplar

Sir Ranulph Fiennes is a record-breaker and endurance expert. He has run seven Marathons on seven continents in seven days, and he has reached both the North and South Poles of the planet on foot. In May 2009, six years after a heart bypass operation, after a heart attack and two earlier failed attempts, at the age of sixty-five, he has conquered Mount Everest (8,850m). He has done

these things to raise money for the charity 'Marie Curie Cancer Care' because his mother, his first wife and two of his sisters died from cancer within an eighteen month period. He wants people suffering from terminal illness to have quality nursing care, either in a hospice or in their own homes.

Endurance is a Christian virtue which Seniors are often called upon to demonstrate. Jeremiah was a prophet who had to endure a run of four bad kings, who not only paid no attention to his message but they tried to assassinate him. He showed endurance.

A lifetime of faithfully serving God does not guarantee earthly security! Saint Paul had to endure incredible physical abuse and persecution. Read this:

> I have been put in jail more times. I have been beaten with whips more and have been in danger of death more often. Five times the Jews gave me thirty-nine lashes with a whip. Three times the Romans beat me with a big stick, and once my enemies stoned me. I have been shipwrecked three times, and I even had to spend a night and a day in the sea. During my many travels, I have been in danger from rivers, robbers, my own people, and foreigners. My life has been in danger in cities, in deserts, at sea, and with people who only pretended to be the Lord's followers. I have worked and struggled and spent many sleepless nights. I have gone hungry and thirsty and often had nothing to eat. I have been cold from not having enough clothes to keep me warm.
>
> *2 Corinthians 11:23-27 (CEV)*

But near the end of his life he wrote to his young friend Timothy:

> I have fought the good fight, I have finished the race, I have kept the faith. Now there is in store for me the crown of righteousness.
>
> *2 Timothy 4:7-8 (NIV)*

Feats of endurance, especially in advancing years and for the benefit of others, are to be commended. Sir Ranulph receives adulation, celebrity status and Royal recognition. And so he should, for he has performed spectacular feats of endurance at an advanced age and for a good cause, to help other people.

But all of us, especially all Seniors, are called upon to show endurance in our circumstances, and endurance in our faithfulness. All who remain faithful to our Lord Jesus will receive more enduring recognition from the highest authority!

This is what James wrote to his Christian friends:

> Blessed is the man who perseveres under trial, because when he has stood the test, he will receive the crown of life that God has promised to those who love him.
>
> *James 1:12 (NIV)*

Prayer

Lord, bless those in their first lap of the Christian race of life. Grant peace in times of turmoil, forgiveness for sins and clear direction for life.

Lord, bless those in the middle of the Christian race of life. Grant persistence in the midst of pressures at work and at home. Give strength to those competing to keep a job and caring for a family. Bless those burdened with many responsibilities and loads.

Lord, bless those near the end of the Christian race of life. Some find it hard to keep going when they are older; some feel lonely, many suffer a range of physical illnesses, some feel forgotten by family or separated from friends.

Lord, bless us and all Seniors, those weary in the later stages of the race of life.

Lord, give us persistence in our prayers and devotions, even if we feel isolated.

Lord, give us faithfulness that we may continue to pray for others in greater need.

Lord, give us endurance, that the good work you started in our lives may continue.

Lord, give us assurance that though we may sometimes forget you, your nature is never to forget us.

Lord, give us the certainty that we will receive the Crown of Life – for we truly do love you, through Jesus Christ our Lord and Saviour.

Amen.

Seniors should be Generous

See God's assessment of generosity

Immunising children is marvellous. With just a few doses given to children, vaccines, acting on the body's immune system, can prevent deadly diseases for a lifetime. In the last fifty years one deadly disease – smallpox – was eradicated. Disability and death from polio, measles, tetanus and whooping cough have been reduced, and other good vaccines are already available.

Immunisation was a special interest and passion of mine, and I even edited and wrote a book on the subject.[22] Therefore, in January 2010, I rejoiced when I heard that the Bill and Melinda Gates Foundation were giving $10 billion (£6.25 billion) for vaccines and immunisation programmes in poor countries. It is estimated that this could save eight million lives in the next decade. There has never been such a large single donation for a specific objective. It is an incredible gift.

Giving money is not a new phenomenon, and the Bible encourages people to give to God and to poor people in need – not just a tenth of their disposable income but, as Paul reminds us, "God loves people who love to give." (2 Corinthians 9:7, CEV)

Jesus certainly knew about money. Some people tried to trick him with a coin, and a disciple betrayed him for cash.

---

[22] 'Immunization, principles and practice', Dudgeon and Cutting; Chapman & Hall (1991); ISBN: 0-412-23540-4

He watched people giving their offerings at the Temple and made some important observations.

> So when you give to the needy, do not announce it with trumpets, as the hypocrites do in the synagogues and on the streets, to be honoured by others. Truly I tell you, they have received their reward in full. But when you give to the needy, do not let your left hand know what your right hand is doing, so that your giving may be in secret. Then your Father, who sees what is done in secret, will reward you.
>
> *Matthew 6:2-4 (NIV)*

On another occasion...

> Jesus sat down opposite the place where the offerings were put and watched the crowd putting their money into the temple treasury. Many rich people threw in large amounts. But a poor widow came and put in two very small copper coins, worth only a fraction of a penny. Calling his disciples to him, Jesus said, "Truly I tell you, this poor widow has put more into the treasury than all the others. They all gave out of their wealth; but she, out of her poverty, put in everything – all she had to live on."
>
> *Mark 12:41-44 (NIV)*

Jesus implied that God judges generosity not by the amount given but the amount that is left over and that we keep for ourselves. According to the Sunday Times 2009 'Rich List', Bill Gates was still worth some £28 billion. God's evaluation of giving is so counter-cultural that, in his eyes, the most generous donor of our era, Bill Gates, gave less than the widow who gave so little. But what she gave left her completely impoverished and completely dependent on God.

Our God who "sees in secret" challenges the giving of each of us, including pensioners in more wealthy situations. We are to compare ourselves not with those on the Rich List but with the sacrificial giving of the poor widow.

Prayer

Lord God, give me wisdom and generosity in how I use the
money you have entrusted to me.

Lord, it is easy to make excuses for not giving to those in
need, thinking that it will be misused.

Lord, my family and I have legitimate needs. Help me sort
out needs from wants.

Teach me the difference between the **cost** of things and the
value of things that money cannot buy. Thank you,
Lord, for the priceless gifts of your love and grace. May
my life overflow with true gratitude that will make me
generous to share what I have, and what I am, with any
in need.

Amen.

"There are no pockets in a shroud."

You can't take your financial treasures with you!

The richest relative – ever

An old man was brought in to Mercy Hospital and
taken for emergency coronary surgery. The operation went
well and, as the groggy old man regained consciousness, he
was reassured by a Sister who was waiting by his bed.

"Mr. Smith, you're going to be just fine. The surgical
team did a wonderful job, and your heart has a new lease of

life," said the nun, gently patting his hand. "We do need to know, however, how you intend to pay for your stay here. Are you covered by insurance?"

The old man clutched his chest. "No, I'm not," he whispered hoarsely.

"Can you pay in cash?" persisted the nun.

"I'm afraid I cannot, Sister."

"Well, do you have any close relatives?" the nun asked hopefully.

"Just my sister in New Mexico," he volunteered, "but she's a humble spinster nun."

"Oh, I must correct you, Mr. Smith. Nuns are not spinsters. They are married to God."

"Wonderful!" said Smith. "In that case, please send the bill to my brother-in-law."

Seniors, Where is Your Treasure?

Bank robbery

An armed gang broke into a bank in London and stole security boxes that were stored there. The total value of the loss was over £5 million. One old lady lost her jewellery that was estimated to be worth half a million pounds.

She cried, "Everything I had was in there. My whole life was in that box!"

Really? How sad!

We all need enough resources to live reasonably, and that is why money is important and useful, but of limited value in life. When we get older we like to hold on to some things that give a different sense of security. We all have some things that we particularly treasure. Many such things have emotional and sentimental value that cannot be measured in pounds, dollars or rubles, and carry no insurance or re-sale value. Often these things are different from the things that we treasured when we were young – a letter, a photograph, a soft toy, a gift from someone special, but still they are our 'treasures'; they have a meaning and worth beyond any commercial price.

Another day, a man stopped Jesus and asked, "Teacher, what good thing must I do to get eternal life?"

Jesus said, "Why do you question me about what's good? God is the One who is good. If you want to enter the life of God, just do what he tells you."

The man asked, "What in particular?"

Jesus said, "Don't murder, don't commit adultery, don't steal, don't lie, honour your father and mother, and love your neighbour as you do yourself."

The young man said, "I've done all that. What's left?"

"If you want to give it all you've got," Jesus replied, "go sell your possessions; give everything to the poor. All your wealth will then be in heaven. Then come follow me." That was the last thing the young man expected to hear. And so, crestfallen, he walked away. He was holding on tight to a lot of things, and he couldn't bear to let go.

Matthew 19:16-22 (The Message)

Jesus also said:

Do not store up for yourselves treasures on earth, where moth and rust destroy, and where thieves break in and steal. But store up for yourselves treasures in heaven, where moth and rust do not destroy, and where thieves do not break in and steal. For where your treasure is, there your heart will be also.

Matthew 6:19-21 (The Message)

What is your treasure? What is my treasure?

Your lasting treasure is what you have given away! When we get older we begin to recognise that our friends, our families, our faith, these are the most valuable things in life. Indeed our lasting treasure is what we have given away in time, commitment and sharing. These will outlast us!

What is the 'jewel box' in your life? Where is your 'treasure' stored?

Jesus also said, "Come and follow me, leave the rest of your stuff, and all your wealth will then be in heaven."

Prayer

Lord Jesus, as we get older we get possessive about things. We think, "I have earned it. I have looked after it carefully and treasured it all these years. I deserve it." Lord, then I remember, "Don't be foolish! You brought nothing into the world. You cannot take it with you when you die, which might be quite soon."

Lord Jesus, please give me a new sense of values – nearer to your sense of values. Help me to put my relationship with you in the central place in my life, so that all the other things and all other relationships will fall into their rightful places.

Amen.

Seniors, Remember to Cancel Your Credit Cards before You Die!

My Great Aunt died this past January, and her bank billed her for February and March for their annual service charges on her credit card, and added late fees and interest on the monthly charge. The balance had been 0.00 when she died but was now somewhere around 60.00 – so I called the bank.

Me: "I am calling to tell you that Beatrice Jones died back in January."

Bank: "The account was never closed and the late fees and charges still apply."

Me: "Maybe you should turn it over to the debt collections."

Bank: "Since it is two months past due, the collectors have already been informed."

Me: "So, what will they do when they find out she is dead?"

Bank: "Either report her account to frauds division or report her to the credit bureau, possibly both."

Me: "Do you think God will be mad at her?"

Bank: "Excuse me?"

Me: "Did you just get what I was telling you – the part about her being dead?"

Bank: "Sir, you'll have to speak to my supervisor."

The supervisor came on the phone.

Me: "I'm calling to tell you that Beatrice Jones died back in January with a zero balance."

Supervisor: "The account was never closed and late fees and charges still apply."

Me: "You mean you want to collect from her estate?"

Supervisor: (stammers) "Are you her lawyer?"

Me: "No, I'm her great nephew."

I gave the name and address of her lawyer.

Supervisor: "Kindly fax us her Death Certificate."

Me: "Sure. I will send you a copy right away."

The fax number was given, and the conversation continued after they received the fax.

Supervisor: "Our system just isn't set up for death. I don't know what more I can do to help you."

Me: "Well, if you figure it out, great! If not, just keep billing her. She won't care!"

Supervisor: "Well, the late fees and charges will still apply."

I thought, "What is wrong with these people?!"

Me: "Would you like her new billing address?"

Supervisor: "That might help..."

Me: "The Memorial Cemetery, 10 Forest Road, Plot Number 57."

Supervisor: "Sir, that's a cemetery!"

Me: "Correct, you got it! The bank must have an agent there to make collections!"

Seniors, Look at Lending, Borrowing, Debt – and Giving!

Many Seniors are justifiably cautious about borrowing and lending, especially with money. Most Seniors have come through periods of limited income. In earlier generations many would not buy something until they had saved up for it and could pay cash in full. But now, in the era of the credit card, the majority of people in the UK live on credit. Many refund promptly, but some overuse, cannot pay back, land in debt, and modern debt collectors are as sharp as Shakespeare's Shylock.

Recently, lending and borrowing have led humans into a new dimension of trouble. Individual people, then businesses, banks and whole countries took on unrealistic loans that have resulted in a widespread economic crisis. The response of politicians? More borrowing, on an astronomical scale! Politicians who stated that they were being "prudent" were apparently selling gold reserves and borrowing to support a range of government schemes which could not be afforded. The crisis will certainly hit the poorer people and poorer nations most severely, but everyone will bear some of the cost and pain. It seems quite likely that the debts will not be paid back for several generations. Some say our great grandchildren will be paying off our debts! This is not a legacy to be proud of.

Another Shakespearian character famous for giving advice was old Polonius. His hot-headed son Laertes, is about to set out for Paris, and Polonius counsels him with this famous aphorism. [23]

> "Neither a borrower nor a lender be,
> For loan oft loses both itself and friend,
> And borrowing dulls the edge of husbandry[24]."

Long ago the Bible warned against borrowing and specifically against lending money at interest. Here are just two quotes:

> If you lend money to my people, to the poor among you, you shall not deal with them as a creditor; you shall not exact interest from them.
>
> *Exodus 22:25 (RSV)*

> O Lord, who may abide in your tent? Who may dwell on your holy hill? ... [Those] who do not lend money at interest, and do not take a bribe against the innocent.
>
> *Psalm 15:1,5 (NIV)*

Today many of us borrow and pay back with little thought about these warnings and implications. Indeed we could not have bought a house without a loan. Some Christians who have saved money try to ensure that it is invested with 'ethical' companies. But has the Church turned a blind eye and become involved in the investment business? Has it rationalised that borrowing and lending is essential for commercial enterprise? Clearly money lending is one of the oldest professions, and simple borrowing and lending was

---

[23] Hamlet Act 1, scene 3, 75–77.
[24] domestic thrift

common in Jesus' day, and not specifically condemned. Remember Jesus' story:

> Suppose one of you goes to a friend in the middle of the night and says, "Let me borrow three loaves of bread. A friend of mine has dropped in, and I don't have a thing for him to eat."
>
> *Luke 11:5-6 (CEV)*

However Jesus' main emphasis was always on **giving**. Seniors should be the first to take a fresh look at what he said about money and material things, referred to as 'stuff' in modern jargon. Paul reminded people:

> Remember that our Lord Jesus said, "More blessings come from giving than from receiving."
>
> *Acts 20:35 (CEV)*

Generosity is God's policy!

Lord, grant us wisdom and generosity with the money entrusted to us.

Amen.

Giving, the secret of joy[25]

Life is for living, so live it and see
Just what a wonderful world it can be
When you let go of things that annoy
And start to discover the secret of joy.
Life is too good and too sweet and too brief
To waste upon grievances, grudges and grief.

Life is for giving, so give of your best.
Keep nothing back and your days will be blessed.
Give time and give money,
    give thanks and give praise.
You'll get it all back in mysterious ways.
Life was not meant to depress and destroy,
No, life is for giving and giving is joy.

---

[25] Author unknown, possibly partly based on words of Patience Strong, the pen name for Winifred E. May.

The Answer to the Debt Crisis?

It's a slow day in a damp little Irish town – the rain is beating down and the streets are deserted. Times are tough, everybody is in debt, and everybody lives on credit.

On this particular day a rich German tourist is driving through the town, stops at the local hotel and lays a €100 note on the desk, telling the hotel owner he wants to inspect the rooms upstairs in order to rent one for the night.

The owner takes out some keys and asks the temporary porter to show the visitor what is available. As soon as they have walked upstairs, the hotelier grabs the €100 note and runs next door to pay his debt to the butcher.

The butcher takes the €100 note and runs down the street to repay his debt to the pig farmer.

The pig farmer takes the €100 note and heads off to pay his bill at the supplier of feed and fuel.

The guy at the Farmers' Co-op takes the €100 note and runs to pay his drinks bill at the pub.

The publican slips the money along the counter to the local prostitute drinking at the bar, who has also been facing hard times and has had to offer him 'services' on credit.

The hooker then rushes to the hotel and pays off her room bill to the hotel owner with the €100 note.

The hotel proprietor places the €100 note back on the counter.

At that moment the German traveller comes down the stairs, picks up the €100 note, states that the rooms are not satisfactory, pockets the money, and leaves town.

No one produced anything. No one earned anything.

However, the whole town is now out of debt, the 'feel-good factor' is flowing, and everyone is looking to the future with a lot more optimism.

Is that how the bailout package works?

Debt, the Destroyer

It was a Saturday morning in February 1998 in Bradford, UK, when John Kirkby received a distressed phone call. Something told him that this was a real emergency. An old couple, Mark and Eva, were in a desperate state; they were on the point of eviction. Mark, who had been confused for months, was due for a hospital psychiatric assessment, and Eva had tried to shield him from their financial plight. Their old car, on which they were dependent, needed a costly repair, and they had taken a short-term loan. Then their rent and fuel bills had gone unpaid and they borrowed money again but were unable to pay it back. They were paralysed by fear because of their escalating debts and the threats and demands from those to whom they owed money.

The day before John's visit, the Bailiff (a legal officer in cases of debt) had arrived, expecting to take over the property and furniture, and was dismayed to see that the couple had not packed anything. He was a reasonable man and even helped them get a stay order until 10:30 on Monday. When John arrived on Saturday, Eva was distraught. Until the Bailiff called she had kept the desperate situation from her agitated husband. It took John more than an hour to calm them down and get enough information to mount a challenge to the repossession. It was winter. They had no one to help them and nowhere to go. They were in shock and could not comprehend what was happening to them. They were decent Seniors who had fallen on hard times and did not know what to do.

John, who had set up the charity 'Christians Against Poverty' (CAP), had the experience and knowledge to resolve their difficulties and offered to represent them in court on Monday morning, free of charge. He felt a deep sense of care and compassion for this desperate old couple, and verses from the Bible's Book of Proverbs rang in his mind:

> Don't take advantage of the poor just because you can; don't take advantage of those who stand helpless in court. The LORD will argue their case for them and threaten the life of anyone who threatens theirs.
>
> *Proverbs 22:22-23 (GNT)*

In court on Monday, the landlord's lawyer started a rant about what hopeless tenants the old couple had been. The Judge silenced her after two minutes and gave John the opportunity to explain the circumstances and plead for leniency. A thirty-day suspension order was granted, and John ran to the Bailiff's office to hold off the eviction. CAP took over the responsibility and made contact with all creditors, negotiated more reasonable terms of repayment and worked out a simple and possible budget for the old couple. Their relief was incredible and they proved to be very faithful with their simple budget. Within four years they had paid back their debts and, with the help of CAP, had moved to sheltered accommodation. In response to the practical Christian love and witness shown by John and his team at CAP, Mark and Eva had given their lives to Jesus and joined a local church.

John and his CAP colleagues have intervened in this way in thousands of cases. They believe deeply that their success is truly a work of God's Spirit for those in distress.[26]

Redemption: a story of justice, compassion and a saving intervention

The woman had been caught red-handed; a bag of unpaid-for items hidden under her raincoat at the exit from the supermarket. She was single, a mother with a couple of kids to feed on a minimum income. But, as the prosecution lawyer stated in court, the evidence was clear and convicting. Judgement was necessary and the sentence was passed: "£200 to pay or two weeks in prison." Full of contrition the woman pleaded for mercy as she had no money and did not want to leave her children to the care of anyone else, but the judgement and sentence had to stand. It was the Law.

Then the Judge came down from his bench, took off his robe and wig and went and stood by the plaintiff. He pulled out his wallet, peeled off four £50 notes, handed them to the woman, asked her to pay the fine and leave the court a free woman.

The price for her freedom had been paid!

---

[26] 'Nevertheless' (The story of Christians Against Poverty), 11th edition, 2011; John Kirkby; CAP Books; ISBN: 978-0-9546410-4-7. See website: capuk.org.

The two stories – the first absolutely true, the second possibly contrived – speak of 'redemption', which has several meanings. It can mean the free gift of release from slavery or some other form of bondage. For Christians it is the message of God's redeeming love through believing in Jesus. For people who 'mess up' – and that's all of us who "sin and fall short of God's high standards" – the unique path to pardon is through the voluntary self-sacrifice of Jesus for others. Amazing! A mystery but true.

Prayer

So thank you, God, for redemption, and thank you also for CAP. May John Kirkby and his team release many more people from the bondage of debt and fear.

Amen.

Seniors should "Go the Second Mile"

Paul Brand, surgeon

Paul Brand was a brilliant scientific observer and surgical innovator. He worked as a missionary surgeon at the Christian Medical College in Vellore in South India. He was the first person to note that the damage to the hands and feet of those suffering from leprosy, the loss of fingers and toes, was not because of the direct effect of the infectious bacterium, but because the germ affected the nerves and took away the protective sensation of pain. The shortening and loss of fingers and toes was the result of numerous small injuries.

Paul also noted that there was a consistent pattern to the paralysis of leprosy; it always affected some groups of muscles but spared others, and this resulted in the typical 'claw hand' deformity. He devised an operation transplanting some of the tendons from the unaffected group, giving the leprosy patients a useful functioning hand again. For this work he was awarded the Hunterian Professorship of the Royal College of Surgeons of England.

Later he was horrified to learn that some of the leprosy patients he had successfully treated were in difficulty because they could not get work. Moreover, because they no longer had deformed hands they could no longer beg! He devoted much of the rest of his life to rehabilitation. He wanted to ensure that after the surgical treatment the patients could look after themselves and earn a living. He devised tools that suited their hands and protected them against injury because they had no feeling. He wanted his patients to enjoy a full life in all its dimensions: physical, social and spiritual. Many successful surgeons would have been satisfied to accept the accolade of "innovative master surgeon" and leave the follow up to others. But Paul Brand, a diligent disciple of Jesus, took to heart his command in the Sermon on the Mount seriously to "go the second mile".

Here is what Jesus said in the Sermon on the Mount:

> If anyone forces you to go one mile, go with them two miles.

Matthew 5:41 (NIV)

Eugene Peterson paraphrased Jesus' words like this:

> "And if someone takes unfair advantage of you, use the occasion to practice the servant life. No more tit-for-tat stuff. Live generously."

Matthew 5:41 (Message)

You do not have to be an innovative surgeon to "go the second mile". Many Seniors have the time, experience and desire to give practical help and encouragement to those who are in need. Keep your eyes open every day for opportunities.

Prayer

Lord God, thank you that even Seniors have chances to live the servant life. Sometimes when someone asks for help, it is hard enough just going one mile. Please give me the generosity of heart, the strength of body and the determination of spirit to go the second mile. Make me eager to help before I am asked.

Amen.

Seniors can Model Gratitude and Positive Thinking

I am so thankful...

For the old wife who says, "It's just scrambled egg on toast tonight."

Because she is home and cooking, and not out at the bingo or in the geriatric ward.

For the old husband who is still cluttering up the house.

Because many women of my age have lost their men. (Puny gender that they are!)

For the dog hairs all over my clothes and settee.

Because it means I have a faithful four-legged companion for company.

For the fistful of pills that I have to swallow down every day.

Because without them my aches, pains, wheezing and cough would be unbearable.

For my deafness.

Because I can switch on my hearing aids when I want to hear something, and switch off when the noise is too harsh or I don't want to hear that grumble again!

For my old friends who are going deaf.

Because they cannot hear the embarrassing noises from my bowel.

For food allergies, both real and imagined.

Because I can refuse to eat a number of things I don't enjoy eating.

For the heavy traffic that slows the road right down.

Because I show my Senior Travel Pass, let the driver take the strain and speed up the Bus Only lane.

That I could give my car to my grandson who needs it to go to work.

Because I don't have to fill it with fuel and get it through the MOT (roadworthy) test.

For my failing memory so I cannot remember quite a lot of people.

Because there are a number of petty minded, irritable people I'm glad to forget.

For the amount of tax I have to pay.

Because it means I still have a pension that is significant enough to incur tax. (Think if I lived in a country with no pension?)

For the abuses practised by our newspapers (though I do not approve of them).

Because they are still free to expose fraudulent Members of Parliament. (There are still plenty of other fraudulent rogues they could go after!)

For the asylum seekers who pour into Britain.

Because we are still considered a country that stands for justice and mercy.

For weather of rain and showers, and unpredictable 'bright intervals'.

Because it gives us something to talk about and it makes Britain into a "green and pleasant land".

For my online friends who send me many jokes, make me laugh and remind me of their love!

Lord, bless them, and keep them sending me thoughts and funnies. Thank you!

It is better to be satisfied with what you have than to be always wanting something else.

Ecclesiastes 6:9 (GNB)

Grant us the Eyes to See

Denis Burkitt lost one of his eyes in an accident when he was a child, but he was determined. He went on to achieve his ambition and trained as a doctor and a surgeon. He was disqualified from joining the British Colonial Medical Service because he had only one eye, but after being an effective army surgeon in the Second World War he was able to join the Colonial Service and worked in the medical college in Uganda.

While there he made some careful observations on children with unusual tumours of the face and neck. One day two experienced surgeons from different parts of Africa joined him on his ward round. One of them said he regularly saw such facial tumours in children. The other said that in a lifetime of work he had never seen such a condition. Denis applied for the smallest research grant ever, only £25! With that he sent postcards to many doctors all across Africa. The cards had pictures of Ugandan children with facial tumours and a single question, "Do you see children with this sort of condition?" He mapped the yes and no responses and saw a remarkable geographic pattern.

Careful follow-up demonstrated that this was a special sort of cancer with geographic and environmental limits. Also it was associated with suppression of the immune system, malaria and infection with the Epstein-Barr virus. Burkitt then helped to develop a very effective chemotherapy treatment. His simple but brilliant research has been internationally acclaimed. It was the first sort of cancer shown to be associated with an infection and immunodeficiency, and it is now known as Burkitt's Lymphoma. He was a devout Christian and a humble man who was still researching and preaching into his eighties.

When he lectured about this unusual lymphoma, Burkitt often declared, "I thank God that he enabled me to see with one eye what many others could not see with two!"

In the Old Testament (2 Kings 6:8-17) you can read that the Prophet Elisha had special insight. When Israel was at war he helped the King of Israel by warning him when and where the enemy king was laying ambushes for him. Eventually the enemy king realised that Elisha was the cause of this divine espionage; he tracked him down and surrounded him with his army. Elisha's servant panicked and asked what they could do.

> "Don't be afraid," the prophet answered. "Those who are with us are more than those who are with them."
> And Elisha prayed, "Open his eyes, LORD, so that he may see." Then the LORD opened the servant's eyes, and he looked and saw the hills full of horses and chariots of fire all around Elisha.
>
> *2 Kings 6:16-17 (NIV)*

We can often look at something and not see what is really going on. Like Elisha's servant, we may be blind to the protection that God has provided or the direction God is pointing. Many doctors had seen children in Africa with severe tumours of the face, but Denis Burkitt's enquiring mind and open vision helped him to look beyond his job as a surgeon. He found that the special tumours had a particular geographic pattern, linked with infections, and were treatable by drugs. Whatever our age or stage, we must remain sensitive to what God can reveal to us or say to us.

Prayer

Dear Father God, King Solomon said, "Where there is no vision the people perish!" (Proverbs 29:18, KJV)

Please open our eyes in faith to see your purpose at work, in our lives and in the world.

Enlighten our minds and fire hearts with a vision to see what you want us to do even in later years.

Strengthen our hands to serve you and to serve others.

Amen.

Oh, that I could see better!

I took my four-year-old grandson to the optician to pick up his new glasses. The glasses were prescribed "to help him read and be able to see the computer better".

When we got back home, he got on the computer to play a game. In a few minutes he called me and said there was something wrong with his glasses.

I asked him what the problem was and he said, "I still can't read."

Later, much later...

My grandson went with me to the optician to get my new glasses to help me to read better. When I got home I called my grandson and said, "The glasses are no good. I still can't read properly".

"Look, Grandad," he said, "they do help a bit. It's not really the fault of the glasses. They correct your presbyopia and astigmatism, but you still have cataracts, glaucoma and macular degeneration."

Old Timer with Great Eyesight

An old man was a witness in a burglary case.

The defence lawyer asks Sam, "Did you see my client commit this burglary?"

"Yes," says Sam , "I saw him plainly take the goods."

The lawyer asks Sam again, "Sam, this happened at night. Are you sure you saw my client commit this crime?"

"Yes," says Sam, "I saw him do it."

Then the lawyer asks Sam, "Mr Samuel Johnson, listen, you are eighty years old and your eyesight probably is bad. Just how far can you see at night?"

Sam replies, "I can see the moon. How far is that?"

Seniors can be Magnanimous

Nelson Mandela

Be selective in what you save in your memory bank!

Nelson Mandela was an icon of forgiveness and reconciliation. He was brought up in a grossly unjust country under the yoke of apartheid. As a young man he rebelled against this but armed himself with education in his fight against injustice. For a time, he followed Gandhi's non-violent resistance, but became convinced that the brutal apartheid regime would not respond to this. So he rose to be head of the armed wing of the Africa National Congress. He was caught and convicted of sabotage and spent twenty-seven years in prison, mostly in the notorious Robben Island. As a 'dangerous criminal' he was subjected to the harshest regime, deprived of most comforts, and could only receive one letter and visit in six months. The prison also became 'Mandela University', and he studied for a Bachelor of Law of the University of London as an 'external student'! He was released in 1990, aged seventy-two, and four years later became the first President of South Africa by a fully representative election. Through the amazing Truth and Reconciliation Commission the communities put earlier injustices behind them.

One of the keys to a happy and peaceful old age, or advanced Senior years, is to have a healthy bank account. Not money, though that can help, but a good balance and reserve in your memory bank. If you have made good and regular deposits, you can withdraw when losses or loneliness catch up with you. So, deposit a lot of happiness in the memory bank. Do not store up the problems and hurts! 'Count your blessings' and remember to thank the people who have given you good things to deposit. Have an active account and make happy deposits as often as possible. They are your wealth to use 'on a rainy day'.

Paul the Apostle was a man who knew a lot about physical suffering and had been in prison several times, usually on trumped up charges. Writing as an old man from prison in Rome to his friends in the town of Philippi, another place he had been in jail, he concludes:

> Finally, brothers and sisters, whatever is true, whatever is noble, whatever is right, whatever is pure, whatever is lovely, whatever is admirable – if anything is excellent or praiseworthy – think about such things and the God of peace will be with you.
>
> *Philippians 4:8-9 (NIV)*

This is the way we should store positive material in our memory banks if we are to enjoy our senior years. Look at Mandela. He had not stored up bitterness and revenge in his heart. After years of injustice and deprivation he did not take it out on the prison guards or the judges who had sentenced him. What generosity of heart! He wiped the hurt and hatred from his memory bank.

Three short quotes from his many magnanimous words:

"As I walked out the door toward the gate that would lead to my freedom, I knew if I didn't leave my bitterness and hatred behind, I'd still be in prison."

"If you want to make peace with your enemy, you have to work with your enemy. Then he becomes your partner."

"If there are dreams about a beautiful South Africa, there are two roads to that goal: Goodness and Forgiveness."

Mandela walked those roads in an exemplary way. He was a magnanimous Senior!

Prayer

Lord God, thank you for being a forgiving Father. Thank you for the assurance that when we truly repent, you truly forgive and forget our sins.

Lord God, forgive me even though I find it hard to forgive others for real or imagined injuries.

Lord God, sometimes I believe I have forgiven, but I find it harder to forget, and this damages my relationships. Help me to wipe out and delete bitter memories from heart and mind.

Lord God, make me alert to see good and noble actions and store these in my memory.

Lord God, make me sensitive to, and thankful for, all that is done for me. Help me to both store and speak my gratitude.

Amen.

Seniors can be Organ Donors

Have you heard the story of the blind boy who sold fruit outside a railway station? In the rush and bustle someone knocked over his little stand and scattered the apples across the pavement. One busy man took time to help him gather the fruit, set up the display, and bought several, only to discover that he had missed his usual train home.

The little blind boy stammered his thanks and concluded, "Hey mister, are you Jesus?"

My friend Tony is one of very few people in my life about whom I have been tempted to ask that question. He is a man of deep convictions, a member of the Christian Society of Friends, the Quakers, with a special love for peace. As a young doctor, and newly married, he appealed against conscription into the army and was sent to work with the British scientific team in Antarctica for nearly two years! Siberia is warm by comparison. (It is a good thing that his wife shares a deep Christian faith, for it cannot be easy to live with a person of such high and strong convictions.)

Since 'retiring' Tony has done countless things to help the most vulnerable of people, those who really need loving and personal care. He worked with a team caring for children with HIV infection in Zaire (now the Democratic Republic of Congo), he taught physiology at the impoverished, beleaguered Palestinian medical college in Gaza, he helped drug offenders in their struggles to get free from the habit, and he is now a member of a group that befriends and monitors sex-offenders when they are released from custody, in this way reducing re-offending.

Now, pushing eighty, Tony has donated one of his kidneys to an unknown person in renal failure who is on the waiting list for organ transplantation. He successfully went through a battery of tests. Although he has had a double hip replacement himself, he walked miles every day to keep himself fit and to "give the recipient the best chance of a healthy organ".

Is it wise or worthwhile for Seniors to donate organs?

The answer is yes, but it depends on your state of health and not your age, explains Mr Fernando, consultant transplant surgeon at The Royal Free Hospital, in London. All organs age, but the rate at which they age depends on lifestyle factors and the presence of diseases like diabetes and high blood pressure. Kidneys from older donors do better than heart or lungs. Every donor is put through stringent tests to ensure that both kidneys function well, that there is no hidden virus disease, and the heart and circulation are fit for the operation. The lifespan of a donated kidney from an altruistic living person is fifteen years, and a number have already been functioning for thirty years. There are over eight thousand people in the UK waiting for organ transplants so healthy Seniors are welcome on donor panels.

A study from the prestigious Mayo Clinic in the USA compared the results from younger donors (seventeen to forty-nine) with older donors (fifty to seventy-one) and showed that patient and graft survival was excellent in both groups.[27] Often kidneys from older donors may be matched to older patients with kidney failure. But in 2008, when, Patrick Graham heard that his nephew Richard Foley, nearly forty years his junior, was in desperate need of a kidney transplant, he wasted no time in contacting the transplant coordinator in Glasgow. At seventy-three he became Scotland's oldest kidney donor.

To become a live donor is a courageous, altruistic selfless decision. Even if the recipient is another Senior, it can make an incredible difference to the quality of the life of an elderly person in kidney failure. Life on regular renal dialysis is very hard and restricted.

Check it out on *www.uktransplant.org.uk*. Think about it, discuss it and register!

---

[27] 'Patient and graft outcomes from older living kidney donors are similar to those from younger donors despite lower GFR'; De LA VEGA L.S.P. et al.; in Kidney International (2004) 66, 1654–1661; from the Mayo Clinic, USA.

The Ultimate Donation

In August 1998, my wife and I celebrated our fortieth wedding anniversary and the gift of a wonderful family. We gathered in Edinburgh: four children, their spouses, nine-and-a-half grandchildren, and a number of close friends. After a small thanksgiving service and a meal, the family set out for a holiday together. We were staying on the shores of Loch Ard in the beautiful countryside of Perthshire, Scotland. On day three, after a Safari Park picnic, our son-in-law Richard cycled into the town of Stirling to shop – and tragedy struck our celebration.

While cycling, Richard was hit from behind by an inexperienced eighteen-year-old driver. He received a severe head injury and was air-lifted by helicopter to the Neurosurgical Unit in Glasgow. The duty surgeon told us that although Richard's external injuries were slight, his brain scans showed serious damage and he would probably die within twenty-four hours. We were appalled and grief-stricken. Our daughter Catriona's fortitude and faith were amazing. She and Richard had four children aged twelve, ten, eight and six. She immediately said that she wanted Richard's organs to be used in transplant operations for other people and she wanted the children to come and say goodbye. The words she spoke to them explaining the situation were inspired and beautiful. She stayed with Richard until his brain-dead body, on a respirator, was taken to the operating theatre to retrieve the organs. Through his death, six other people were offered the gift of renewed life. Our anniversary holiday had been a tragedy, but the family rallied together and some good came from the calamity.

One year later, in August 1999, a man in Northern Ireland wrote a letter of thanks to the person he knew only as "Richard's widow".

> "I was so breathless that I needed extra oxygen twenty-four hours a day. I could not even tie my own shoelaces, but now after the transplant I am off on my cycle."

The man was Gerry McCormick, who had received Richard's right lung. Gerry suffered from a progressive lung disease that was crippling and killing him. He had to take an oxygen cylinder with him everywhere and had been told that without a transplant he had only weeks to live.

Gerry was dyslexic, left school at fourteen and was apprenticed to a joiner. However, he was remarkable. With a blend of technical skill, honest hard work, vision, wisdom and an ability to get on well with people, he built up a large construction business that was widely respected for its quality and reliability. He had also worked to heal the division in Northern Ireland, helping and encouraging those from both sides of the divided community in his town, Derry (Londonderry).

Gerry's letter to Catriona took several months to traverse the confidential transplantation network, but Catriona responded eagerly. Letters and family photos were exchanged, and an invitation followed. Exactly two years after Richard's death and the transplantation, the two families met and spent three days together. Catriona, her four children, and her parents travelled to Gerry's home. Both families were nervous as they knew little about each other. Because Gerry and Catriona were both very positive people, the time together was a great success. We were united by a living lung that had rich memories of the past, gave vitality for the present, and hope for the future.

The parable

There is a certain parallel between a fatal illness that can only be cured by the donation of a vital organ, a heart or lung, and the core message of the Christian faith. The disease is so drastic that only death and donation of a good organ from another person can work the cure. The gift of a vital organ is priceless, but one life must end before another can be saved.

The fundamental Christian message has three parts.

- All people suffer from a deadly disease.
- This requires a radical remedy which has been provided by God.
- But people have to give informed consent and accept the gift.

WE ALL HAVE A DEADLY DISEASE, AN INCURABLE ILLNESS

It is called sin.

God's standard is very high and demanding! How does God define sin?

Jesus said the first and most important commandment is this: love the Lord your God with all your heart, and with all your soul, and with all your mind, and with all your strength. The second is this, Love your neighbour as yourself. There is no commandment greater than these.

Mark 12:30-33 (NIV)

Sin is not only obvious evil which grabs media attention. Sin is not only armed robbery or trafficking in drugs and people. Examine Jesus' key commands carefully. Sin is not loving God **totally**. Sin is not loving other people, even unlovely people, as much as you love yourself. It is impossible to fulfil these demands! Sin is failing to achieve what God considers most important, indeed essential. God's standard is impossibly beyond ours. We **all** fall short. Because we sin, we are not fit for his kingdom. We have a fatal illness and cannot cure ourselves.

A REMEDY IS NEEDED, AS RADICAL AS A HEART TRANSPLANT

This is our only hope. The whole attitude of our hearts is such, that we are naturally and deeply selfish. When we examine God's commands we see there is no cure in our own strength. This is not a case for a simple remedy, no place for DIY treatment, trying a bit harder to fulfil God's commands. In fact, we need divine intervention. For this condition the cure is so radical, only a transplant will do. Nothing short of a new heart will do the job, and for a heart transplant, someone has to die to provide the cure. This is where God intervened. There is a divine donor; Jesus died for sinful men and women, for each of us, and God accepts that.

> You see, at just the right time, when we were still powerless, Christ died for the sinful. Very rarely will anyone die for a righteous man, though for a good man someone might possibly dare to die. But God demonstrates his own love for us in this: While we were still sinners, Christ died for us.
>
> *Romans 5:6-8 (NIV)*

THE RESPONSIBILITY OF THE PATIENT

These are the days of shared responsibility in medical care. No operation should be done without the patient being told what will happen, what the risks are, the potential benefits and what the alternatives are. The patient must sign the informed consent form. Obviously only a patient who believes in the treatment will sign the form.

The recipient has a responsibility, and we know that before Gerry McCormick had his operation he had been fully informed about the operation and knew the risks. There was the risk of the operation, the risk of immune rejection and of serious infection after the operation. But weigh this against the alternative: progressive disease and death. Gerry knew the risks, but he said, in effect, "For the last few years I have tried all other treatments to no avail. Yes, I need new lungs; indeed I believe a transplant is my only hope. I will sign the consent form." But he could have refused. Some patients do.

With regard to the fatal condition of sin, Jesus tells us that God has intervened with a saving remedy, but to use the remedy we have to believe and respond. This is how Jesus' disciple John described God's intervention:

> For God loved the world so much that he gave his one and only Son, that whoever believes in him shall not perish, but have eternal life. For God did not send his Son into the world to condemn the world, but to save the world through him.
>
> *John 3:16-17 (NIV)*

So this is the incredible story of God's love. It is his free gift, but it cost Jesus his life. God's gift is a truly life-giving therapy, but it also requires a responsive recipient.

We cannot earn or buy eternal life, but we can believe and accept it. So do it now!

Prayer

Lord, my God and Father,
Lord Jesus, my Master and my Saviour,
Holy Spirit, my helper,

- I accept that I have a deadly disease. I cannot fulfil your commands. I fall short; I sin.
- I thank you for your intervention, for your love, for your unconditional gift and your divine donation, the life and death of Jesus for me.
- I confess I need your help. I say, "I believe." I accept your gift of eternal life in Jesus' name.

Thank you!
Amen.

Contact the Author

The author would be happy to receive comments or communications about this book or series at:

william.cutting@talktalk.net